A Devil to Ride

By Patricia Leitch and published by Catnip:

For Love of a Horse
A Devil to Ride
The Summer Riders
Night of the Red Horse
Gallop to the Hills
Horse in a Million

A Devil to Ride

Patricia Leitch

CATNIP BOOKS
Published by Catnip Publishing Ltd
14 Greville Street
London
EC1N 8SB

This edition published 2011

3 5 7 9 10 8 6 4 2

Text copyright © Patricia Leitch, 1976
The moral right of the author has been asserted.

Cover design by Chris Fraser
Cover photography by Karen Budkiewicz

A CIP catalogue record for this book is available from the British Library.

ISBN 978-1-84647-107-0

Printed in India

www.catnippublishing.co.uk

FOREWORD
by Lauren St John, author of *The White Giraffe*

For Love of a Horse, the first book in the *Jinny* series, is my favourite pony book of all time. I read it for the first time when I was about eleven and every bit as horse mad as Jinny, and it's hard to overstate how much impact it had on me and how much I related to the story and to Jinny's relationship with her horse. It didn't matter that Jinny lived at Finmory on the Scottish moors, and spent her days passionately trying to save or tame a chestnut Arab mare, and I lived on a remote farm in Africa and spent my days trying to save and train a black stallion, it seemed to me that the way we thought, felt and dreamed about the horses we loved was identical.

Imagine having a best friend who thinks about riding exactly the way you do; who gets into the same kind of disastrous, scary or embarrassing situations and suffers the same kind of highs and lows, and who just happens to have the horse of your dreams. That's what Jinny and Shantih were for me. Over the years, scores of other fans of the series have felt the same way. You will too. And if you're anything like me, you'll be drawing pictures of Shantih and pinning them up on your bedroom wall, reading each book at least five times, and wishing and dreaming that you had a chestnut Arab mare just like Shantih and could gallop across the moors with Jinny, mysterious, magical Ken, and all the other characters who make up Jinny's world at Finmory.

You're in for the ride of your life. Enjoy!

Lauren St John
London, 2010

One

The chestnut Arab bucked suddenly, heels high, her head tucked between her front legs, her body twisting as she bucked again and again. Jinny Manders clutched the front of the saddle with both hands, tightened the hold of her bony knees and clung on desperately. She didn't know what else she could do.

'Whoa, Shantih, whoa the horse. Steady, Steady.'

The words were jolted out of Jinny's mouth and scattered into the silence of the April evening. Bramble and Punch, the two Highland ponies who were grazing in a far corner of the field, didn't even flicker their ears at the sound of Jinny's voice. The waves lapped up the deserted sands of Finmory Bay, the moors and mountains that surrounded Finmory House were wrapt in their own mysteries. For hundreds of years they had seen humans come and go while they stood still. The skinny girl and the violent Arab horse were no concern of theirs.

'Whoa. Steady. Stop it. Stop it. Steady now.'

After the fourth buck the Arab paused. Jinny relaxed her hold and patted the sweated neck. Shantih bucked again; heels flung skywards, head and neck disappearing from in front of Jinny as she went soaring through the air, her long, straight, red-gold hair flying out behind her.

Jinny landed on her feet as neatly as a cat, Shantih's reins still clasped tightly in her hand. It had happened so often to her in the past few weeks that Jinny was beginning to wonder if she couldn't work in a somersault before she landed. But she only wondered that to stop herself from thinking too much about what would happen if her mother or father or Petra, her elder sister, were to see one of Shantih's explosions. Mike, her younger brother, had seen Shantih rearing with Jinny one night.

'She is pretty wild, isn't she?' he'd said.

''Course not,' said Jinny sharply. 'If you knew anything about horses you'd know that she's just fresh.'

'That's not what your book says,' replied Mike. 'It says rearing is a dangerous vice. They can fall over backwards and *churumphch*. Strawberry jam!'

'She doesn't always rear. Sometimes she only bucks. And anyway I'd jump off before she came down.'

'Rather you than me, but you'd better be a bit careful hadn't you?'

'You may not have noticed, but it is a horse I'm riding – not a knitted donkey. No one expects a pure-bred Arab to behave like an ancient pony.'

'Well, be careful you don't let Mum see you,' Mike had replied, and Jinny had been doing her best to exercise Shantih in the early mornings or late evenings when her family were less likely to be about. It was so unlike her brother to tell anyone to be careful that Jinny knew he must have been impressed by Shantih's rodeo.

'Why are you so silly?' Jinny asked her horse.

Shantih sighed gustily and rested her head against Jinny's arm. She was calm and gentle now, all her temper vanished. Her huge Arab eyes with their long lashes looked mildly around her, her muzzle, pushing hopefully against Jinny's hand, was as soft as plush velvet.

'Don't think it,' Jinny told her, doing her best to make her voice sound severe. 'You are getting nothing from me. Not a thing. Pig of a horse. I hate you.'

But Jinny didn't. She loved her. Loved her so much that there was nothing else in her life that really mattered, only her drawing and Shantih. There were the other things that Jinny really took for granted – her family and her home. Even living in the Scottish Highlands surrounded by sea and sky and open

11

country was beginning to be the way things always were, although it was only last summer that Mr Manders had stopped being a probation officer in Stopton and had brought his family away from the city streets and the continual traffic to make a new life in the Highlands. They had come to live in Finmory House, a large, grey, stone house standing by itself between the hills and the sea. Mike and Jinny rode two trekking ponies to school in Glenbost village, and Mr MacKenzie's farm was the only other house near Finmory.

Standing and scratching Shantih's neck, Jinny remembered how she had first seen the Arab in a circus, billed as "Yasmin, the Killer Horse". So many things had happened between the night when Jinny had fallen in love with Shantih and last month when at last the Arab had belonged to her.

'And now you're mine,' Jinny told Shantih, 'so why do you have to start all this nonsense? You are a nit.'

Jinny put the reins back over Shantih's head and remounted. She knew from the light that it was getting late, too late to start another fight to try and make Shantih trot in a circle. Jinny walked her on a loose rein round the field. Once Shantih realised that there were to be no more attempts at schooling, she pricked her ears and walked out willingly, whinnying to the Highlands as she passed them but not trying to join them.

'I'll ride you round once,' Jinny told her. 'That's the right thing to do. "Always finish your schooling on a happy note so that both rider and mount feel satisfied with what they have achieved",' Jinny quoted from her book. 'So that's what we'll do. Not that we've achieved much,' she added, knowing that if she tried to take Shantih round the field twice there wouldn't be a happy note.

Jinny's book also said that if your horse was misbehaving you were to use your legs strongly, backed up by your stick. When Jinny had backed up her strongly used legs – which she took to mean kicking – with a stick from the hedge, Shantih had gone mad. Her first furious buck had sent Jinny smashing into the ground; then, rearing and bucking, she had galloped round and round the field. When Jinny had at last managed to grab her reins and hold on to them, Shantih had stood wide-eyed and shaking with fear. Her chestnut coat had been curded with sweat and she had flinched away from Jinny's touch.

It was the first and only time that Jinny had tried to use a stick on her.

'She thought she was back in that circus. She thought I was the ringmaster that whipped her,' Jinny had accused herself as she broke the stick into pieces and threw it away.

After this, the only solution that Jinny could think of was to hold on while Shantih reared or bucked.

'If only I could get better at staying on then she would get fed up with trying to get me off and start to behave herself,' Jinny reasoned. But somehow Jinny nearly always ended up on the ground.

'Jinny,' called a voice from the field gate.

Jinny dismounted quickly, just in case, and led Shantih towards the gate.

It was Ken. He was standing by the hedge, almost invisible in the gathering spring dusk. His black sweater and faded jeans blended into the shadows of the hedge; his bony face was calm and still and his fair hair grew long past his shoulders.

The Manders had first got to know Ken when he had been on probation for being with other boys who had broken into a Stopton warehouse. When his probation was over Ken had said to Mr Manders, 'I'd nothing to do with it.' 'I know,' Mr Manders had acknowledged.

Ken had arrived at Finmory on the Manders' first day there, bringing Kelly, a grey-thatched, yellow-eyed dog, with him. Ken was seventeen. His parents had washed their hands of him except to send a monthly cheque to him through their bank. 'I'll stay, if you'll have me,' Ken had said, and they had all gladly accepted his offer. He worked with Mr Manders in the room that they had converted into a pottery, knowing far more about it than Mr Manders did, and he had dug a kitchen garden out of Finmory's overgrown wilderness.

'Feed us all,' Ken said. 'What do you want to go on eating animals for when the earth's bursting itself to feed us?' Jinny had never known Ken to eat anything that came from an animal.

It was Ken who had helped Jinny to save Shantih. Ken who had saved Jinny's life.

'How's she doing then?' asked Ken, reaching out his long-fingered hand to gentle Shantih's head.

'I've just finished riding her,' Jinny said hurriedly. 'She's looking better, isn't she?'

'Beautiful,' agreed Ken. 'Rather see her without all that gear strapped on to her though.'

'I've got to ride her,' exclaimed Jinny. 'No one has a horse and doesn't ride it.'

'There was some old bloke somewhere used to read from the Bible and his horse came to listen.'

'I expect he was a saint,' said Jinny, knowing Ken's old blokes. 'And I'm me. I'm going to ride everywhere on Shantih, trekking and cross country and dressage...'

Jinny saw clearly the flat dressage arena, the white test markers, the crowds round the corded barrier. She felt Shantih stop correctly in front of the judges as she lifted her stick and touched the brim of her bowler, remembering to smile.

'Mike seemed to think you were using her as a means of suicide, and your Mum sent me to say what about the milk?'

The dressage arena vanished. Jinny began to say,

'What did Mike tell you . . .' then clapped her hand to her mouth. 'I forgot again!'

'I'll go.'

''S OK. Mr MacKenzie will have left it for me in the milking shed.'

'You going to ride over?'

'She's done enough for tonight,' Jinny said, not looking at Ken. 'I'll give her some nuts and then I'll get the milk.'

Jinny led Shantih up to her loose box. Years ago when Finmory had been a farm this outhouse had been stables. The Manders used part of it as a feed house and tack room. There were two stalls for Bramble and Punch, the ponies they had borrowed during the off season from Miss Tuke's trekking centre, and opposite the stalls was a loose box that was now Shantih's.

The Arab barged through the doorway, knowing that she was going to be fed. Jinny took her tack off and gave her some nuts.

'I shouldn't be giving you anything,' Jinny told her, tipping the scoop of pony nuts into the trough. Shantih paid no attention to her, but crunched her way steadily through them while Jinny took a dandy over her.

When she had turned Shantih out with the black Bramble and the white Punch, Jinny hung over the field gate watching her roll then trot across to the other ponies. The heavy bulk of the two Highlands made Shantih seem more like a fairytale horse than ever,

Jinny thought. She was all lightness and air as she danced her way across the field.

'Haven't you gone for the milk yet?' accused Mike. 'There isn't a drop left and Dad's wanting coffee. He sent me to hurry you up.'

'I'm just going,' said Jinny, and she set off along the track to Mr MacKenzie's farm. Petra, who was nearly fifteen, went to Duniver Grammar and stayed at the school hostel during the week, but Mike, who was nine, and Jinny, who was eleven, both went to the school in Glenbost and took it in turns to fetch the milk from the farm. When it was Mike's week it was like being back in Stopton with regular deliveries, but when it was Jinny's her family realised that they were living in the remote Highlands.

'But I do try to remember,' Jinny explained. 'I've drawn a picture of Buttercup VII. Mr MacKenzie says he knows it's her because of her leer. And I pin it on my bedroom door when it's my week. But when I've forgotten, I can't remember and it's only when I see Buttercup VII leering at me that I remember I've forgotten.'

Mrs Manders listened to Jinny's excuses.

'Couldn't you always go at the same time every day?'

'I wish I could,' agreed Jinny. 'I do wish I could. But it's a waste of time making timetables for myself. I never ever manage to stick to them.'

As Jinny wandered her way to the farm she wondered if timetabling Shantih might help to calm her down a little. She didn't want to calm her down too much – only enough for Jinny to stay on her.

Every morning an hour's hacking, Jinny thought. *Or maybe two hours. Then when she's settled I could try lungeing her again.* She had tried lungeing Shantih three times already but each time had been disastrous, with Jinny on the end of the clothesline being dragged round the field by a mad, dervish horse.

But perhaps if I did it regularly, every single day of the Easter holidays, it might improve her, thought Jinny. *I'll make a timetable and I'll stick to it.* She saw the timetable in her mind's eye. She would draw pictures round its edges, pictures of Shantih doing turns on the forehand, collected canters, and half passes.

But the bubble burst. A thousand timetables would make no difference. They would only mean that Shantih would be able to throw Jinny off at more regular intervals.

'I don't know enough,' Jinny muttered desperately. 'I don't know the right things to do. My riding just isn't good enough. I've never had any proper lessons and sitting on Bramble isn't really riding. Not like riding Shantih. Books are no good. Reading them it all sounds so easy but they're no use when I'm flying through the air,' and Jinny groaned aloud. She knew only too well that each time Shantih played up and got away with it she was learning that she could do exactly as she liked with her.

'What I need is someone to help me. Someone who knows the right way to do things. If only I had a different family,' longed Jinny, and saw herself as a Pony Club child walking beside her mother as they went down to the field together to lunge Shantih. 'Don't worry, dear, I'll soon take the tickle out of her feet, then you can get up and I'll lunge you both for a bit. Soon tighten up your seat,' breezed Jinny's Pony Club mother.

'Would you look where you're going?' warned Mr MacKenzie, as Jinny nearly walked straight into him. 'Your head's wasted, lass.'

'Sorry,' gulped Jinny, suddenly realising that she had reached the farm.

'I'll be giving you a penny for them.'

'Not worth it,' said Jinny. 'Sorry I'm late for the milk.'

'Now that would be nothing unusual. It's got the chilblains waiting for you in the milk shed.'

Jinny fetched the full cans of milk.

'I hear you've been having a wee bit of trouble with your horse?'

Jinny scowled suspiciously at the old farmer. Sometimes she thought he knew everything that happened at Finmory, though how he found out she could never understand.

'A rare battle you're having with her and her winning every time. You'll be for working on the circus act I'm thinking, her being a circus horse?'

'Is that so?' said Jinny.

'Aye, it might be. I told you well it's a man that one's needing.'

'If you mean one of your sons knocking her about that is the last thing she needs, no matter how often you tell me.'

Mr MacKenzie stared out over the hills, sucking his pipe.

'Is it more a wee touch of class you have in mind for her?'

'What?'

'Then I've the very news for you. You'll be knowing Craigvaar House?'

'Yes,' said Jinny. Craigvaar was a modern, snow-cemmed house with a housekeeper to keep it smooth and cared for while the family who had built it lived in Sussex. Since the Manders had been at Finmory there had never been anyone except the housekeeper staying at Craigvaar. It stood alone on a part of the moor that Jinny didn't know very well, but she had ridden past it once or twice when she had been out on Bramble. She had looked curiously at the clipped hedges, neat flowerbeds and reaches of smooth lawns. Standing up in her stirrups, Jinny had thought that she could make out several loose boxes almost hidden from view by rhododendron bushes, but she had never seen any sign of horses.

'Well, it's like this – you'll be having the new friends for the holidays. There's word in the village today that the Burnleys are coming for Easter.'

'Are there any children?'

'A wee bit more than children. Clare will be thinking herself a young lady now and Spencer's away to Oxford, so I hear, so that'll be him out of the short trousers.'

'More Petra,' said Jinny. 'Not much good to me.'

Mr MacKenzie regarded her disapprovingly.

'It's the terrible speed you have on you,' he said. 'Would you be waiting a minute until I get the words out of my mouth. I haven't reached the horses yet.'

'Horses!'

'If you were in the know with the horsey set the way you're not,' teased Mr MacKenzie, 'whenever you were hearing the name Clare Burnley you would be saying, "Not *the* Clare Burnley," and I'd be telling you, "The very one."'

'Never heard of her,' said Jinny. 'Is she a show jumper?'

'Indeed she is, and winning the big cups at all the shows in the South. She'll be one of these superstars, I'm thinking. Always with the winners.'

Jinny narrowed her eyes and considered the farmer. She knew him well enough by now to suspect that he was pulling her leg.

'Now don't be looking at me like that. It's the truth I'm telling you. Clare Burnley herself stood where you're standing now, telling me all about the rosettes and cups she was always winning at the big shows.'

Jinny grinned.

'Now don't you be laughing. Clare can stay on a horse, not like some I could mention.'

'Are they bringing their horses with them?'

'Two. She'll be for the Inverburgh Show, winning all the cups there with her grand horses.'

Jinny could tell from the tone of the farmer's voice that he wasn't too keen on Clare, but she thought that if Clare won cups for show jumping she must know quite a bit about horses.

'Do you think she'd help me with Shantih?'

'Well, I wouldn't like to say that. Don't you forget it's the toffs you're talking about when you're talking about the Burnleys.'

As Jinny walked home she pictured Clare Burnley as dark and dashing, confidently riding a bay thoroughbred and wearing a black jacket, cream breeches and gleaming black boots.

'Camel's milk?' asked her father, who was going bald on top but had a thick beard the same colour as Jinny's hair. 'Been to the Sahara for it?'

'No,' said Jinny, 'just to the farm *but* . . .' and she launched into a Technicolor description of Clare Burnley and her horses.

'This going to be your Easter thing?' asked Ken, but not really asking, more as if he knew before anything happened how it would all be in the end.

'Oh yes,' Jinny assured him. 'It's a smashing chance. She's bound to know all about schooling green horses.'

'Bad enough sending kids to school, never mind horses,' said Ken.

'How are you going to get to know her?' asked Mrs Manders.

'Oh, I'll ride over. I expect she'll have heard about Shantih and be pleased to meet me,' replied Jinny as casually as she could, trying not to think too much about her own jeans and trainers compared with Clare's breeches and boots – and not looking at Ken.

Two

Jinny decided to ride to Craigvaar the next Saturday afternoon. She asked Mike to come with her. He said he would and went to catch Bramble and Punch.

'Where are you going?' Petra asked. Jinny told her. 'I'll come too,' said Petra.

'But you never ever ride,' Jinny said, staring in dismay at her sister. 'I mean you never do. So why should you want to today?'

'All the more reason why I should have a turn,' replied Petra.

'Mike's coming,' said Jinny. 'And we're only going to look at the house. Mr MacKenzie doesn't think the Burnleys have arrived yet. So you needn't think you'll meet them. And if you come there aren't enough horses.'

'You can ride Shantih,' said Petra.

'But there aren't enough saddles,' stated Jinny desperately. The last thing she wanted was for Petra to see her being bucked off Shantih and go and tell their mother about it.

'Mike can ride bareback,' organised Petra. 'He often does.'

'But we're going now,' said Jinny, 'and you haven't done your practising.' Petra was going to be a piano teacher when she left school and she practised faithfully every day. 'Surely you don't want to come when you haven't done your practising. You'll fail your exam.'

'Don't worry, I'll do it when I get back.'

'Oh don't be so mean,' said Jinny. 'What do you want to come for? I'm telling you the Burnleys haven't arrived yet. You just think they're upper class and posh, the kind of people you want to get to know so that you can talk about them at school. But you needn't bother coming today because they won't be there.'

'What's the matter?' asked Petra, giving her sister a hard stare. 'Are you afraid to ride Shantih?'

'Don't be so silly! Of course I'm not afraid. I just don't see why you want to come with us today,' and Jinny marched down the garden to the stables. She could see it was going to be one of those days when everything went wrong. 'Well, you can groom Bramble yourself,' she shouted back over her shoulder.

Mike had caught the ponies and brought them in to their stalls.

'I've got them,' he said when he saw Jinny taking down a halter.

'Petra's coming,' said Jinny darkly.

'Petra!' exclaimed Mike in amazement. 'But she never does.'

'It's the Burnleys,' said Jinny. 'She wants to get to know them so they can all be frightfully frightful together. Well, I shouldn't think they'll be a bit like that. Horsey people aren't. And they may not even be at Craigvaar.'

'You're not going to ride Shantih?'

'Yes I am,' said Jinny defiantly. 'Of course I am.'

'Then we'll never reach Craigvaar. All we'll do is watch her throwing you off.'

'That's only when I'm schooling her,' snapped Jinny. 'She's quite different when we're going for a ride.'

'Now let's get a move on,' said Petra, coming into the stable. 'We want to get there while it's still dry. What shall I do?'

Mike handed her a dandy and reluctantly Jinny went off to catch Shantih.

Shantih, waiting at the field gate, whinnied when she saw her. She pushed her head into the halter and crushed through the gateway before Jinny could get the gate open properly.

'Steady, steady,' muttered Jinny, shutting the gate while Shantih pranced at the end of the rope in her eagerness to follow the Highlands.

'Now behave yourself,' said Jinny sharply. 'Petra's coming with us and we don't want to let her see you carrying on.'

Shantih broke into a trot, dragging Jinny towards the stable. Her head was high in the air, her hoofs tit-upping on the ground as Jinny dug her elbow hard into her shoulder to stop her cantering.

'Oh stop it, Shantih,' Jinny muttered between clenched teeth. 'Behave yourself. Stop being such an idiot.'

Shantih took no notice of her. She charged through the low stable doorway and, with a clatter of hooves on the stone floor, stormed her way into her box. Jinny just managed to avoid being crushed against the door.

'Gosh,' said Petra. 'She is fresh. Is she always like that?'

'Like what?' said Jinny. 'If you mean alive, yes she is always alive and that's the way I want her to be.'

Shantih stood alert and tense while Jinny groomed her. She stuck her head into the air, refusing to let Jinny put her bridle on.

'Can't you manage?' asked Petra.

'Of course I can,' said Jinny, standing with the bridle in one hand while Shantih's giraffe neck stretched out of reach above her.

'Here,' said Petra, bossing her way into the box, and because she was taller than Jinny she was able to put her hand over Shantih's nose and hold her head down while Jinny slipped her bridle on.

'Thanks,' said Jinny ungratefully.

'That's all right,' said Petra. 'Miss Benson was only saying the other day that even when I don't know much about a thing she could always rely on me to be sensible.'

Jinny groaned aloud. There was no doubt about it, her sister was sensible.

Jinny slid the saddle onto Shantih's hard, high back and buckled up the girth. Mike and Petra had taken their ponies out into the yard and Shantih pushed against the box door, clattering it with her forehooves, trying to follow them.

'Oh, wait a minute,' shouted Jinny, her voice muffled under the saddle flap as she struggled to tighten the girth. 'Now get back and wait a moment.' Jinny yanked at Shantih's bit and she skittered back in a wild flurry of mane and tail.

'Right,' said Jinny and led her out to where the other two were already mounted.

'Which way are we going?' asked Mike.

'Along the road to Glenbost and then up the track to Craigvaar,' said Jinny, pulling down her stirrups. The other way was to go straight onto the moors and to ride over the hills to Craigvaar, and Jinny didn't fancy taking Shantih straight onto the moors. She needed the trot along the road to settle her.

Jinny swung herself into the saddle and felt Shantih sink back on her quarters. Then the chestnut neck arched above her as Shantih reared. Automatically Jinny leaned forward. She found her other stirrup and as Shantih touched down she closed her legs against Shantih's sides and urged her on.

'Ready?' asked Mike.

''Course,' said Jinny. 'She'll jump over the top of you if you don't get a move on.'

Punch laid back his ears and kicked out peevishly as Shantih came plunging into him.

'Oh for goodness' sake get a move on,' said Jinny, tugging at Shantih's reins to keep her behind the ponies. She knew that once they were trotting Petra would need to concentrate on her posting and wouldn't be able to look behind to see what was happening and Jinny thought that would be for the best.

They rode past Mr Mackenzie's farm and out onto the road to Glenbost.

'OK to trot?' asked Mike, and without waiting for an answer he roused Punch into a trot.

Jinny sat down hard in the saddle and kept Shantih behind the rounded rumps of the Highlands. 'You're not going in front,' she told her horse. 'I know what you'd do if you got in front, next thing we'd be galloping over the horizon. This is quite fast enough.'

A gusting wind blew shreds of black cloud over a scoured sky. The mountains were leaden and rooted, foursquare, into the moorland. Moors, sky and mountains were etched shades of grey.

As Jinny rode, the tight knot in her stomach unclenched a little. She felt Shantih relax, her trot become more even, her shies at blown strands of dead bracken or sudden birds were less violent. She was beginning to accept the bit and move less rigidly. Jinny clapped her sleek neck and laid her hand on the rounded bulk of the mare close behind her saddle. Perhaps it was a good thing that Petra had wanted to come with them. Riding with both ponies was giving Shantih more confidence. Jinny knew that if she had been by herself Shantih would have been bucking and rearing long before this.

The scarlet Post Office van came rattling towards them. The Highlands trotted sedately on. Shantih stared, pop-eyed. She cantered on the spot, her tail kinked over her back, snorting through wide nostrils as the van passed her, then she plunged after the ponies, shrieking to them not to leave her behind.

'She hardly looked at it,' Mike called back.

Jinny grinned. 'There's a brave horse,' she praised. 'Well done the clever old horse.'

But Jinny knew that if she had been by herself she could never have got Shantih past the van. They would have been galloping flat out back to Finmory by now. Knowing this made the day seem more grey than ever. The mountains squatted like monster toads against the skyline, their heavy gloom weighing down on Jinny as she rode. There was just a chance that the Burnleys might have arrived at Craigvaar. Should they be there, this wasn't the way Jinny wanted to meet them, all cluttered round with her family. If they met Clare Burnley now, Jinny knew who she would talk to and it wouldn't be herself; it would be Petra.

Jinny scowled at her sister's back. The triangle of Petra's neck-scarf fitted neatly under Petra's dark curls, her anorak and corduroy trousers looked smart and sharp-edged the way clothes always did on Petra. Jinny's long tails of red hair snarled in the wind, her anorak was crumpled and clinging and the tears in her jeans were cobbled together with Jinny's giant stitches.

But I'm the one who needs to get to know Clare. She's going to help me to school Shantih, Jinny thought. *She must know I'm the one who's mad about horses. She must. She'll see Shantih and know that she's an Arab.*

'I say, that's a stunning Arab you've got there.' Jinny could hear Clare's voice quite clearly. She saw her walking towards Shantih, taking firm strides in her gleaming black boots. She held out her hand to clap Shantih, shook her long dark hair and looked at Jinny with a friendly, level gaze. 'Where did you find this one?' she asked.

A sheep unfolded suddenly at the roadside. Shantih flung herself sideways, Jinny lost a stirrup, banged her nose on Shantih's neck and saw stars.

'Dreaming again?' said Petra scornfully.

'I was not,' denied Jinny. 'You weren't even looking at me so how could you know what I was doing?'

'I don't need to look,' said Petra. 'I know too well.'

'Turn up here?' asked Mike, and they all slowed their horses to a walk as they followed the rutted track over the hillside.

In spite of Jinny's efforts to keep Shantih back, by the time they had reached the turn in the track that brought Craigvaar into sight she was well ahead of the Highlands. Looking down at the detached house with its snow-cemmed walls, immaculately painted woodwork and landscaped grounds, Jinny realised that asking Clare Burnley for help wasn't going to be as simple as it had seemed standing in the kitchen at home. Everything about Craigvaar was smoothed with money. The tennis court, the clipped hedges, weedless gravel paths, formal flowerbeds and modern outbuildings. It all looked as if it were wrapped in an invisible plastic balloon that protected it from the gales and winter snows. As if, Jinny thought, it had been pre-packed in Sussex and dropped down here from a helicopter.

Shantih fretted irritably as Jinny tried to make her stand and wait for the others. The open moorland stretched out around them; space and freedom blew down from the hills where Shantih had once roamed wild with Mr MacKenzie's herd of Shetlands. She stood gazing round through her huge Arab eyes with their fringing of long lashes, drinking in the wild moorland. Jinny knew that if she eased her fingers the least fraction on the reins or tightened her legs on Shantih's sides they would be away, galloping like fire over the moors.

A bit of Jinny longed to urge Shantih forward. She had often galloped the Highlands over the moors but they were native ponies, sure-footed and canny. Shantih would blaze over the bracken and heather, light and swift as fire, and yet Jinny was afraid that she might come down, breaking a leg, which was the same as killing yourself when you were a horse, or flounder into one of the emerald green bogs that could suck a horse down to its death no matter how hard it struggled to escape.

At the back of Craigvaar a large paddock was fenced off from the moorland by white-painted railings that sparkled in the grey light. Jinny looked at it longingly.

And what a car, she thought. Jinny didn't know much about cars, but she did know that the one which crouched opulently in front of the house wasn't a Mini.

But if the car's here, Jinny thought suddenly, *that means* they *must be here too.*

Although the track to Craigvaar was open to anyone, Jinny felt that she was trespassing. She looked quickly round for Petra and Mike.

'Hurry up,' Jinny shouted, but they didn't hear her.

Mike had dismounted and was examining something by the side of the track.

Jinny glanced back at Craigvaar – and started with delight. A girl with curly blonde hair had brought a steel grey horse into the paddock. As Jinny watched she uncoiled the lunge rein from her hand and, flicking a long-lashed driving whip, sent the grey horse round at a walk.

For a second Jinny hesitated, torn between a sudden shyness and the realisation that this was her chance to speak to Clare, for surely the girl must be Clare Burnley. Mike was still crouching down by the side of the track. Petra was leaning over, watching what he was doing. And really Jinny didn't want them with her when she was talking to Clare. Mike didn't matter but Petra would make her say all the wrong things and laugh at her afterwards.

'They can catch me up,' Jinny decided. 'It's their own fault for being so slow,' and she let Shantih trot forward.

Jinny turned off the track to ride down to the paddock and Shantih's trot became a canter, no faster than a slow trot but coiled like a spring ready to burst out into furious speed.

When Jinny reached the paddock the girl paid no attention to her. Jinny's heart sank. If this was Clare Burnley she wasn't in the least like Jinny's imaginings. She was quite fat; maybe not so much fat as solid. Her face was large and round, and her curly blonde hair was stylishly cut and set. Her hand on the lunge rein was firm and unyielding and she grasped the whip tightly in her other hand.

'Hello,' said Jinny, but the girl didn't even look up.

Jinny tried again.

'Hello,' she repeated in a louder voice. 'I do like your horse.' The horse was a sixteen-two hunter with a hogged mane and clipped-out heels. He had the same solidity as the girl, as if they were both building up their weight to be weighed in gold, thought Jinny.

Still the girl didn't reply.

Perhaps I shouldn't interrupt when she's lungeing, Jinny thought and watched silently as the horse walked round obediently. It was obvious that the girl knew what she was doing. The grey horse moved like a lumbering, clockwork toy. Used to the grace and lightness of Shantih, Jinny could only see him as a heavy, half-dead thing.

'Trot,' commanded the girl, and instantly the horse was trotting, his spiky neck arched, his Roman nose tucked in and his hooves' drumbeat steady.

Petra and Mike came into sight and Shantih whinnied to the Highlands through wide nostrils. Still the girl didn't take her eyes off her horse. Jinny swallowed uncomfortably, realising that Clare Burnley was ignoring her on purpose.

Perhaps it isn't that I'm disturbing her. Perhaps she just doesn't want to speak to me, thought Jinny,

35

as Clare brought the horse into the centre of the circle.

'Well, I'll not be disturbing her if I speak to her now,' she decided and urged Shantih closer to the paddock fence.

'He lunges very well,' Jinny said, making sure that her voice was loud enough for Clare to hear. 'I wish I could lunge Shantih like that.'

Without looking up, slowly and decisively Clare Burnley turned her back on Jinny. She gave the grey a piece of carrot then, with a crack of her whip, sent him round in the opposite direction.

Well . . . thought Jinny, but she didn't have time to put into words what else she thought. As the whip cracked Shantih reared straight up. Again Clare flicked her whip over the grey horse's back and Shantih touched down, wheeled round and was tearing over the moor in a panic-driven frenzy.

Clinging to her back, Jinny hardly realised what had happened. She had felt Shantih rear suddenly and with a reflex action had dropped her reins and grabbed a handful of mane and then there was nothing but blinding speed. A blur of speed that flashed the moorland unfocused past Jinny's eyes. There was nothing she could do but sit tight, as, plunging and terrified, Shantih burst through the grey silence.

Sometimes Shantih stumbled on a loose rock or caught her hoof on a heather root or rabbit burrow;

once Jinny felt her quarters sink in the boggy ground and for a fear-bright moment felt her struggling to release herself; but the impetus of her flight threw Shantih forward over all obstacles. Whether she was racing uphill or careering down sheer rocky slopes, Shantih never slackened her breakneck pace. To Jinny they almost seemed to be skimming above the rough ground, like a form of flying.

Gradually Jinny began to get her breath back. She sat up and tried to pull on Shantih's reins, but Shantih's head was stretched low in front of her and Jinny might as well have been riding in a halter for all the difference the snaffle bit made. She looked around, not recognising the part of the moor they were on. Then to her right Jinny saw the silver glint of Loch Varrich. They must have galloped for miles to have reached it. Loch Varrich was beyond the standing stones and not a place Jinny visited very often. There was a deserted eeriness about the sheet of water so alone and so high in the hills. Then Jinny remembered how flat the ground was at the sides of the loch. If she could guide Shantih towards it, she would be able to gallop her in a circle until she came to her senses and slowed down.

To Jinny's relief Shantih plunged on towards the loch. Pulling on one rein with both hands, Jinny managed to turn her and force her to gallop in a wide circle when they reached the shore.

After Jinny had galloped her round several times she felt Shantih's frenzied speed slow down a little.

'Whoa, steady, steady, steady. Whoa Shantih,' cried Jinny, and for the first time since she had started galloping, Jinny felt that Shantih had heard her, remembered that there was someone on her back. Gradually she slowed down to a canter, then to a jagged trot and at last to a walk.

Jinny threw herself to the ground and collapsed. Her legs, worn out with holding on, stretched uselessly in front of her, but her grasp on the reins brought Shantih to a halt. She stood with her muzzle brushing the ground, legs splayed, blood red nostrils gasping at the air. Her face was dark and dripping with sweat and her chestnut coat curded white between her legs and round her belly.

'Oh, horse, horse,' said Jinny despairingly. 'What did you have to go and do that for? And with Petra there to see you. She'll tell them all about it. Make it sound worse than it really was. And Mummy'll start to worry. Oh Shantih, why did you have to be so silly?'

Jinny knew that it had been Clare's whip that had scared Shantih, that she had been given a fright, but she also knew that if her parents got it into their heads that Shantih was dangerous they would stop her riding the Arab.

'You could have broken your legs galloping like that.'

Jinny knelt beside Shantih and examined her legs.

There were a few scratches, and a cut on her off fore was bleeding a little. Jinny looked back over the hillside, the way they had come. She couldn't imagine how Shantih had galloped over such rocky ground without falling.

Jinny dipped her handkerchief into the loch and bathed Shantih's leg. To her relief she saw that the cut was little more than a scratch.

'Your lucky day,' she told the mare. She loosened Shantih's girths, and, walking beside her, led her towards the dark shapes of the standing stones. Once she reached the stones Jinny knew her way back to Finmory.

At the head of the loch there was a clump of pine trees. Not forestry battery trees, but gnarled and real. A hawk was roosting on the dead topmost branch of one of them. It launched itself into the air as Jinny and Shantih approached, sailing over their heads on huge wings – wings that flared across the entire sky, turning upwards at the tips as the bird sailed and swung, riding the air currents. It twisted its head, watching them with a bright yellow eye.

Not an eagle, Jinny thought. *Too much white on it, and yet it's too big to be anything else.*

The hawk tilted a wing and sailed into a distant speck.

'I'll tell them about it,' Jinny said to Shantih, 'when they start going on about you.'

Jinny's family started to go on about Shantih as soon as it saw Jinny. First it was Petra, who had got home before Jinny and given a breath by breath account of Jinny's vanishing out of sight over the moor.

'Well, once she'd started galloping I was enjoying it so much I thought we might as well have a really good gallop,' lied Jinny.

'You did not,' said Petra. 'You should have seen your face. You were scared stiff.'

'I was not.'

'Well, I would have been scared stiff for you if I'd been there,' said Mrs Manders. 'It does look as if you'll need to find someone to help you with Shantih. She's too much for you by yourself.'

'Don't think that that Clare Burnley will be much good,' said Mike. 'There was Jinny going like the wind and Petra screaming and d'you know she never even let on that we were there. Just kept on playing at circuses with that old horse.'

'That's what did it,' said Jinny. 'Shantih thought she was a ringmaster, cracking that whip.'

Mr Manders and Ken had been in Inverburgh buying clay and glazes for their pottery so that they didn't hear about the runaway until the evening.

'Well?' said Jinny's father when he got home. 'Let's hear your version. Mr MacKenzie has given me his.'

He glanced quickly at the sideboard in case there was a letter for him. Since he had been at Finmory, Mr

40

Manders had written a book about the appalling social conditions in Stopton and the hopeless dead-end lives of the young people who were trapped there. Now he was waiting to hear from the publisher, watching for every post in case there should be a letter accepting his manuscript. To her dismay Jinny saw that the only letter for her father looked very like a telephone account.

'Mr MacKenzie seemed to think you galloped from Craigvaar to Loch Varrich?'

Jinny supposed that she had.

'And what would have happened if you'd come off and hurt yourself?'

'But I didn't. That's a hypo-thingy question and Enoch Powell would refuse to answer it. And anyway I wouldn't have been riding Shantih on the moors if Petra hadn't wanted to meet the Burnleys.'

'Don't pass the buck,' said her father in his we-are-not-amused voice. 'One thing for a horse to get a bit of a fright and gallop off. Quite another for it to go mad.'

Jinny felt it was time to remember the strange hawk.

Mike brought down his bird book but Jinny couldn't find a picture that looked like her bird. She spread her arms out, curling up her fingers, and soared round the room.

'It's wings bent back at the elbows,' she said.

'Must have been an eagle,' said Mike. 'That book's

got all the British birds in it.'

'No way,' said Jinny, 'unless someone had been distempering it. And it was huge.'

'A roc?' suggested Ken.

'Maybe,' agreed Jinny. 'And Shantih was Sinbad's flying horse.'

Jinny shivered, reliving the thrill and exultation of her gallop. But really she knew that Shantih had been dangerously out of control, that it had only been good luck that had prevented them from falling. Clare Burnley would never have allowed a horse to behave like that with her.

Jinny remembered the girl's control of the heavyweight horse she had been lungeing. If that had been me standing in the centre the horse would have been doing exactly as he liked, Jinny admitted to herself.

'Flying horse or not,' said Mr Manders, 'there is to be no more of this dangerous galloping about. You must find some way of controlling Shantih.'

Jinny knew from the tone of her father's voice that he meant what he said, and she knew that her mother was right – she needed help to school Shantih.

'Are you sure that Clare Burnley saw us?' Jinny asked hopefully. 'Maybe she just didn't notice us?'

'Blimey,' said Mike, 'we were like a tornado in her back garden.'

'I am sure, sure, sure she saw us,' said Petra.

Jinny fiddled with her hair. Getting Clare to help her wasn't going to be as easy as she had hoped, but it still seemed the only way.

Three

It was a week before Jinny saw Clare Burnley again. Twice she had ridden Bramble over the moors by Craigvaar but there had been no sign of Clare or her horses. Once when they were riding home from school the Burnleys' car had roared past Mike and herself, almost pushing Bramble into the ditch. The man driving it had been so like Clare that Jinny was certain he must be her father. She had caught a glimpse of his fleshy hands gripping the wheel and his stolid, lardy face staring straight ahead.

'Road hog,' Mike had yelled after him.

'He won't hear you,' Jinny said as she soothed Bramble's ruffled dignity. In Glenbost, people on wheels usually made way for people on legs and that was the way Bramble liked it.

'If I shouted in his ear he wouldn't hear,' said Mike.

Jinny agreed, but as the ponies plodded on she couldn't help wondering what it would be like to be sitting at the wheel of a powerful, humming monster, driving straight on, so secure and safe that you didn't even notice that other people existed, never mind worrying about what they might be feeling.

On Friday, Jinny and Mike broke up for the Easter holidays. The last afternoon had been an Open Afternoon when the parents had come to school to see their children's work. When the Manders had first come to Finmory Mr Gorman had been the schoolmaster and the children had spent all their time struggling with endless arithmetic problems, parsing and analysing, reading and spelling, and being belted if they spoke. But now Mr Gorman had retired and Miss Broughton was their teacher, and Glenbost's one classroom wasn't like a schoolroom at all. In some ways it was better than being at home. There was always something new and interesting to do.

Before the parents arrived Jinny had looked round the classroom with a warm satisfaction, like taking bread out of the oven. They'd all done well and their work was there to prove it. Ian MacKenzie's project on Scottish oil – neat and full of facts; Dolina's project that had started off with taking exact notes of everything her family ate for a week and had allowed Dolina to cook traditional Scottish food for them all, then had led on to the problems of food supply in an Indian village; George Cuthbertson had found out about fish farming, and Mike's project on astronomy meant that his stars and planets were pasted over the classroom windows and ceiling.

Jinny had created a world of horses – which hadn't sounded as if it would have much arithmetic in it.

'Can they count?' Miss Broughton had asked.

'Of course,' Jinny had replied indignantly.

'Not in tens then,' Miss Broughton had said. 'They haven't got ten fingers.'

'No,' Jinny had agree, 'but in fives – four hoofs and a head.' So Jinny had had to work everything out for her horses in the scale of five. It also meant that she had been able to paint and draw Shantih whenever she had wanted to.

'What did you like best?' Jinny nagged her parents as they came out of the school together.

'Dolina's shortbread,' teased her father.

'Oh, I mean best of *my* bit,' said Jinny.

'Your pencil drawings of Shantih lying in the straw,' said her mother.

Jinny stood still in delight. 'Fancy you knowing! Just fancy you knowing,' she cried. 'They are my absolutely best thing.' In a few delicate lines Jinny had managed to capture the essence of the Arab; the stored energy packed in her muscles; the vibrant life of her mane and the almost brittle appearance of her fine-boned legs. 'Oh, I am glad you liked them.'

'I need some things from the shop,' said Mrs Manders, and they all walked across the road to Glenbost's one and only shop, Jinny still glowing from her mother's appreciation.

Just before they reached the door the Burnley's car came zooming down the street and stopped in front of the shop. The car doors were flung open and suddenly the village street seemed overflowing with Burnleys. They flooded, loud voiced, up the steps into Mrs Simpson's.

'My dear Mrs Simpson,' cried the slim, black-haired lady as she angled her jaw, leaned forward over the counter, closed her eyes and pressed her cheek against Mrs Simpson's. 'How wonderful to see you again. And how are you? Not a thing has changed. We are all so delighted to be back. I've just been telling Pogo how naughty he has been not coming in to see you before this. When Clare told me that she and Daddy had been at Craigvaar for a whole week and hadn't been in to stock up at your dear little shop I could hardly believe it. I am just not interested in free offers from a supermarket when Mrs Simpson can supply us with anything we'll want.'

'Oh Ma, do try to understand,' Clare Burnley's voice bellowed from her gum boots. 'Mrs Simpson, don't listen to her. Pa had to go into Inverburgh and I was with him so I just popped into the super and bought a very few essentials. I knew Ma would be straight in here the minute she was off the train, I really knew she would.'

'Pogo, do come and say hello again to Mrs Simpson. Coming back to Glenbost would not be the same if you weren't here. I'm forever telling our grocer at home about the wonderful service you give us in Scotland.'

'Gosh, yes,' echoed Clare.

Jinny was standing in the shop doorway, watching in amazement as Mr Burnley, swelling out of his check tweed suit and bulging under his deerstalker, came obediently striding into the shop. A tall boy followed him in.

'Spencer, darling, come and say hello to Mrs Simpson,' Mrs Burnley commanded after her husband had shaken the shopkeeper's hand.

The boy slanted his jaw against Mrs Simpson and held out a limp hand. He regarded her distantly under his lowered eyelids.

'Poor Spencer,' said his mother. 'It is just too, too boring for him. He's only here for one day. Sunday he's off again, aren't you, darling?'

'But Miss Clare will be staying?' asked Mrs Simpson.

'Gosh yes,' said Clare. 'I've got the nags with me. I wouldn't dream of missing the Inverburgh Show. It is my favourite show. I mean to say, even when I'm at Windsor or the White City I'm just wishing like mad all the time that I was at Inverburgh. There is nowhere else like it.'

'Well, I'm sure they'd all be missing yourself if you were not to be going, and that's a fact I'm telling you,' said Mrs Simpson, her mouth smiling at Clare.

'Might give them the chance to win their own cups for a change, eh?' chortled Mr Burnley.

'Have you a nice big box?' asked Mrs Burnley, 'and then we can take everything home together. Now Spencer, you shall choose supper tonight.'

Spencer's lizard eyes flickered over the crowded shelves. His black pencil-line moustache crawled down the corners of his mouth. The expressionless oval of his face was bland as a reflector disc.

'But is there anything here one would want to eat,' he drawled. 'I can't see a single thing.'

'Now don't be so tiresome, darling. I shall choose for you. Can you remember last summer you had those wonderful cans of pheasant?'

Mrs Simpson remembered. She had bought in half a dozen tins knowing that eventually the Burnleys would buy them all.

Mr Manders and Mike went for petrol and Mrs Manders went back into the school to ask Miss Broughton whether there was any more news about the new comprehensive that was being built in Inverburgh.

Jinny just stood and stared while Mrs Burnley filled two boxes with supplies. So could hardly believe that the Burnleys were real.

'What a shower,' said Mr Manders when at last they were driving home. 'They must have spent a fortune.'

'Rather loud,' laughed Mrs Manders.

'Loud,' agreed her husband.

'Good job Ken wasn't there to see them,' said Mrs Manders. 'He would have been telling them what possessions do to you.'

'Too much even for Petra,' grinned Mike.

Jinny was silent. She was staring through the car window, seeing nothing, hearing nothing. Inside her head the Burnleys moved in a golden haze, strong and powerful. They weren't like ordinary people, not people Jinny knew.

'Darling, you shall choose supper.'

'But would one want to eat anything that's here?' said Jinny, moving in her golden dream.

She sat beside Clare as they drove up from the Burnleys' Sussex estate, bringing up Shantih and Clare's horses to win all the cups at the Inverburgh Show.

Astride Shantih, Jinny circled the Burnleys' paddock at a collected canter. Clare stood in the centre, sun glinting on her bright face.

'Gosh,' she enthused. 'That really is the most terrific horse you've got there. Don't mind telling you I'm boringly jealous.'

Mike poked Jinny in the ribs. 'Wake up,' he said. 'We're home.'

Jinny was jolted back to reality, blinking in amazement as she realised her father was stopping the car in front of Finmory.

'D'you think,' Jinny asked her mother, 'you could alter that pair of Petra's cavalry twill trousers for me?'

Arms full of shopping, half in, half out of the car, Mrs Manders turned in astonishment.

'I've been trying to get you to try them on for months!' she exclaimed. 'Whatever made you think of them just now?'

'Dunno,' said Jinny, but she did. Clare had been wearing cavalry twills.

After a mug of coffee, a cheese sandwich and two tomatoes, Jinny went to catch Shantih.

'I'm going to lunge you,' she told her horse. Shantih regarded her with a mild gaze. 'Here you are now, looking as if butter wouldn't melt, but the second I get you out in the field you'll be all over the place like a kite. It's an anchor you need.'

Jinny considered the idea as she groomed. Some kind of hook attached by a rope to the saddle that you could throw into the ground when your horse bolted. The Manders' patent safety horse anchor. But she decided that most people wouldn't be very keen to be seen with it hanging from their horses. She gave Shantih's quarters a final thwack with the duster then went in search of the clothesline and someone to help.

'No,' said Ken. He was in the pottery trying out a new glaze. 'And don't ask me again. If you feel you must make that horse dizzy,' Ken shrugged his bony shoulders, 'then that's up to you. But don't keep asking me to help you.'

'It's to improve her,' pleaded Jinny. 'All the books say you must lunge a horse to improve it.'

'Did you ever,' asked Ken, 'see a horse, left alone to be a horse, going round and round in circles by itself?'

Jinny didn't answer. She banged the pottery door and went to look for Mike.

A quarter of an hour later she was knotting the clothesline onto Shantih's bit ring by herself.

'Clare Burnley didn't need her family to help her,' Jinny told Shantih, 'so I don't see why I should need mine. Her grey didn't need anyone to lead him round so I don't see why you should.'

Jinny led Shantih down to the field. Punch and Bramble, who hadn't been fed that day since they hadn't done any work, came over hopefully.

'Get out of the way,' Jinny warned them, her voice as close to a Burnley boom as she could manage.

The Highlands ignored her. She flicked the end of the clothesline at Punch, remembering too late that that was the one thing that was certain to upset Shantih. Punch only looked surprised but Shantih flung herself away from the rope, almost pulling it out of Jinny's hands.

'Oh, get away with you!' she screamed at the ponies. 'Go on. Go and eat grass.'

Bramble twitched his ears. He had smelt the sugar in Jinny's pocket and was more interested in that than in grass. Jinny picked up a handful of earth and threw it at the ponies. They looked offended. Shantih plunged backwards and this time Jinny dropped the clothesline and Shantih cantered to the far corner of the field.

'Dehydrated dogfish,' swore Jinny, which was what her father said when she was there and he couldn't say what he was thinking. Bramble wuffled at her jeans' pocket and Jinny slapped him hard on the nose. 'Didn't you notice,' she demanded, 'I've just thrown stones at you to scare you off.'

Bramble's feelings were hurt but he knew now that Jinny definitely had sugar.

'Get away,' Jinny yelled. The Highlands ignored her. She ran at them, shaking her arms and drumming her fists against Bramble's shoulder. The ponies took a few reluctant steps away from her but by the time she had picked up the end of the clothesline and wound Shantih in, they were close beside her again.

Jinny stood breathing slowly and deeply, then she dropped the clothesline, caught the ponies by their forelocks and led them out of the field and into their stalls.

'You can stay there and rot,' she told them and,

fastening their headcollars securely, she marched back to the field.

'Right,' she told Shantih, 'let's get lungeing.'

Jinny picked up the clothesline and led Shantih into the centre of the field. She straightened her shoulders, set her feet firmly on the ground and looked sternly at her horse.

'Round you go,' Jinny said, still trying to sound like Clare. She swung her arm out to send Shantih round in a circle but the chestnut shied away from her, turned her head in towards Jinny and stuck her quarters out of the circle.

'That's all wrong,' said Jinny. 'You're not meant to do that. I stand still and you walk round.'

Jinny made a dash to try to get behind Shantih and chase her round but no matter how quickly Jinny moved Shantih was quicker. Jinny could not get behind her. This way and that the Arab and the girl careered about the field.

At last Jinny gave up. She sat down on the grass, her face scarlet, tears of frustration burning her eyes. This was the kind of thing that would never happen to Clare Burnley. At the end of the rope Shantih watched suspiciously, ready to spring away should Jinny show any sign of standing up again. She rolled her eyes nervously, snatched up a mouthful of grass and stood not swallowing it, tense and quivering.

'Oh horse,' said Jinny. She got up slowly and with a

lump of sugar in her open palm walked towards the chestnut. Shantih dropped her head to Jinny's hand, lipped up the sugar and stood crunching it. Jinny fed her more sugar and ran her hand lovingly down her neck, straightening her tangled mane.

'It's no good going on like this, tormenting each other,' Jinny told Shantih bitterly.

'Then come for a ride,' said Ken's voice.

Jinny jumped and looked round. Ken was leaning over the field gate.

'I'd like to try and see your hawk,' he said.

'I can't ride Shantih,' said Jinny, telling the truth because it was Ken. 'She might get a fright and go mad again.'

'I'll ride her,' offered Ken.

Jinny looked at him, wondering if he meant it. Now and again he would take one of the Highlands and go for a ride over the moors by himself, but most of the time he thought horses should be horses not human transport.

Ken sprang over the gate.

'You take Bramble,' he said and took the clothes-line from Jinny and began untying it from Shantih's bridle. 'Watch you don't let Kelly out. I've shut him in the kitchen. He'd want to come with us if he knew.'

By the time Jinny had turned Punch out and got Bramble ready, Ken was mounted on Shantih and waiting in front of the stable for her.

'Your stirrups are far too long,' said Jinny, because it was the only criticism she could think of. Shantih was standing quite still, relaxed and easy.

She would have been mucking about all over the place with me, Jinny thought, settling herself astride Bramble's broad back.

'Loch Varrich?' Ken asked.

'The clump of pines at this end.'

'Know them,' said Ken and he led the way onto the moors.

'Up to the standing stones?' asked Jinny.

'Quicker way,' said Ken, and instead of going up to the stones he followed a sheep track round to their right.

Ken let Shantih walk on a loose rein and when she shied or broke into a canter, he sat there seeming to pay no attention to her. Plodding along behind him, Jinny could just make out the comforting whisper of his voice as he soothed Shantih, gentled her, assured her of the rightness of the world when he was with her. Jinny smiled to herself, feeling her own distress flow out of her into the calm silence of the hills. She let go of her jealousy – jealousy that Ken could ride her horse better than she could. It didn't seem worth bothering about. There was nothing in Ken that said, 'Look at me. See how clever I am.' He only showed you how easy it all was, how simple, if you would only learn to let it be.

The low light from the sun buttered the moors, spreading gold and shadow. The rocks, starved throughout the winter, sucked in the last of the daylight, and the mountains, a hazy mauve, drifted between the sky and the earth.

Ken rode along the flat moorland until they were past the hill crowned by the standing stones, then he turned and followed a sheep track that led over the hills.

'Want to change?' he asked, turning to Jinny.

'Oh, yes please.'

They changed horses.

'Be easy now,' said Ken, taking Bramble on in front. Jinny nodded, left the reins loose on Shantih's neck and sat balanced in the saddle. The Arab walked with a deft, delicate stride, her neck arched, her ears sensitive, the evening light glinting in her luminous eyes, her nostrils wrinkling – yet she was calm and gentle. For the first time Jinny felt there was no fear in her. They rode through pink and golden light, through washes of primrose and ice green; over land so still that Jinny could smell and taste the silence.

Ken's way is quicker, Jinny thought as they came over the rise above Loch Varrich. Far behind them the sea glinted aquamarine against its jet black cliffs but the expanse of the loch had no colour in it. It lay, magic, remote, withdrawn, a stretch of white light in the glowing evening.

They rode slowly down towards the loch. Suddenly Ken stopped, looked back at Jinny and, hardly moving his arm, pointed down to the water.

The hawk Jinny had seen the day before was flying low over the water. It paused, trembling on outstretched wings, hovering kestrel-like above its own reflection, almost motionless. Then, in a fury of speed, it plunged into the loch with talons outstretched, wings sabred back. Water exploded about it as it crashed the surface. It rose with a fish gripped in its feet, gave two beats of its powerful wings, then seemed to shimmer into a crystal, rainbowed jewel as it shook the drops of water from its feathers.

The horses had seen the hawk. They stood as transfixed as their riders.

The hawk, still gripping the fish, flew to the group of pine trees. It stooped low over them, then it seemed to Jinny that for sheer and utter joy it rose up into the air, up through the glowing evening, rising with rapid wingbeats until it was a pinned silhouette far above them, its wings spread wide. It hung there motionless, then came hurtling down, riding the air in wide sweeping spirals, calling all the time with a repeated high-pitched note; lord of the sun's rays; supreme and independent. It swept low over the pines above a mass of branches and twigs, landed on a topmost branch, looked fiercely around, then began to tear at the fish with its hooked beak.

Ken and Jinny waited, watching it. Then, without speaking, they both turned their horses at the same moment and began to ride back to Finmory.

Words were dried up in Jinny. She didn't have any for what she'd seen. Only a brightness that linked the great bird with the way she felt about Shantih; linked the hawk's flight and the Arab's speed. They were almost back at Finmory before she found anything to say.

'It's not an eagle, is it?' she asked, as Finmory's grey, substantial walls, the plume of smoke drifting from the chimney and her mother taking in the washing brought Jinny back into herself.

'An osprey,' said Ken. '*As is the Osprey to the fish, who takes it by sovereignty of nature.*'

Jinny picked on the one bit she had understood. 'But you hardly ever see them in Scotland,' she said. 'Only on that bird reserve place at Loch Garten.'

'But we did,' gloried Ken. 'We did by sovereignty of nature.'

Jinny stood watching Shantih rolling after she had turned her out. Somehow she didn't want to go in and hear her family talking about the osprey. Not just yet. She realised suddenly that she had forgotten all about Shantih being too wild to ride on the moors. She had ridden home as relaxed as if she had been on Bramble.

Wish Clare had been there to see her, Jinny thought

as she turned to wander contentedly back through the garden. Then she stopped stock still.

'I'll bet even the Burnleys would want to know about an osprey,' Jinny said aloud into the darkening evening.

Four

Mr and Mrs Manders, Ken and Mike walked to Loch Varrich the next morning, taking Mr Manders' binoculars with them. The potatoes Jinny had boiled for their lunch and the sausages she had fried were all cold by the time they got back and Petra's fresh fruit salad was tingeing into a rusty brown.

'You've been ages,' Petra said as they came bursting into the kitchen. 'Did you see it?'

But really you didn't need to ask, Jinny thought. One glance at their faces told you that they had seen the osprey. They were all bright with having seen such a hidden thing.

'Two,' said Mr Manders. 'His mate has arrived.'

'They were super,' said Mike.

'I can't believe they've come to Finmory,' said Mrs Manders. 'They can't be the same pair as the ones on the nature reserve at Loch Garten, can they?'

'No,' said Mr Manders, pinching a cold sausage out of the frying pan. 'I read up about them. There are several pairs nesting in Scotland but hardly anyone knows where. The Royal Society for the Protection of Birds publicised the Loch Garten ones so that everyone could have a chance to see them and realise for themselves how important it is to encourage them to start nesting here again. They used to nest all over Scotland but they were wiped out by egg collectors taking their eggs and so-called naturalists shooting them so they could stuff them.'

'They're giving us a second chance,' said Ken. 'To see if we know any better yet.'

'What I know,' said Jinny, 'is that Petra and I have been slaving over a hot stove all morning and you're all so late your dinners are stone cold solid.'

'I thought you'd been slaving over Shantih,' said Petra.

Jinny didn't reply. She had spent most of the morning grooming Shantih, who was in her box looking like a show horse, waiting for Jinny to ride her hopefully in the direction of Craigvaar.

'The most important thing,' Mr Manders said as they sat down to lunch, 'is to keep everything about the ospreys absolutely secret. Not to talk about them at all. Say nothing.'

'Shouldn't we tell the RSPB?' asked Mrs Manders.

'I think we should wait until we're certain they're staying,' said Mr Manders.

'They were adding sticks to their nest this morning,' said Mike. 'I think they'll stay.'

'If they're still around on Monday we'll phone the RSPB, find out who their nearest official is and let him know,' decided Mr Manders. 'Until then not a breath to anyone. Understand?'

''Course I wouldn't say anything,' Mike assured his father.

'Some of the teachers at school would be really interested,' said Petra. 'I shouldn't think they'd tell anyone who would want to harm them.'

'No,' stated Mr Manders firmly. 'Absolutely no one. Tell one other person and they know someone they're certain they can trust so they tell them and in no time we'll have the moors full of birdwatchers. No one meaning to do any harm but nevertheless scaring off the ospreys, stopping them nesting or chasing them off their nest long enough for the hoodie crows to get at their eggs. And there are still some egg collectors who'd take their eggs if they knew they were there.'

Jinny had got up from the table and was filling bowls with Petra's fruit salad.

'Shall we go and see them this afternoon?' Petra asked her.

'Ken and I are going back to put up a hide,' said Mr Manders. 'You can come and help. We've found a cave that should do if we rig up a screen in front of it. Far enough away not to risk disturbing them but near enough to see them with the glasses.'

'You go with them,' Jinny said to her sister. 'I'm going to ride.'

Jinny gave Shantih a final polish before she put her tack on. In the dark box the chestnut's coat rippled with white light when she moved. Her mane and tail flowed silken, almost liquid, and her hoofs were gleaming with Mr Manders' lubricating oil. She had been in her box for most of the morning and wanted to get out. She pushed restlessly against the half door, whinnying to Punch and Bramble, her neck arched and ears straining to hear their reply before she swung away to clatter round the box again.

'What I should do is school you for a bit first,' Jinny told her. 'That's supposed to settle you down. Only it wouldn't. You'd buck me off.'

A bit of Jinny longed to be going with the others to see the ospreys. With her father's binoculars she would have been able to see the details of their feathers, the cold yellow eyes and the black curve of their beaks. But they weren't as important as the chance of seeing Clare.

'Did you know there are ospreys on the hills?' Jinny would say to her, and even the Burnleys would have to be interested in that.

Jinny ran her duster down Shantih's neck for a last time and went out to the tack room to get her saddle and bridle. Ken was standing in the doorway.

'Thought you were all going back to the ospreys,' Jinny said. She wasn't pleased to see him. She knew from the way Shantih had been dashing round her box that she wasn't going to stand calmly in the yard waiting for Jinny to mount the way she had done last night for Ken, and Jinny would rather not have Ken watching the performance.

'We're waiting until it's dusk,' said Ken. He stretched out his arms above his head, spreading his fingers wide. 'How your family does manage to complicate things,' he said. 'There's old Tom dashing around organising us all. Talking about phoning a society, building a hide. *One could not say*, *watching a hawk: I ought perhaps to do this for him*,' quoted Ken, 'but blimey, Tom can. We can't leave anything alone.'

'You don't want the wrong people finding the nest,' said Jinny scraping dried grass off Shantih's bit.

'Then leave them alone,' despaired Ken. 'Oh forget it. I'm only raving on.' He spun round and Jinny thought he was going, but he turned back. 'Where are you off to?' he asked.

'Thought I'd ride towards Glenbost.'

'Craigvaar?'

'Well, why not?' Jinny kept her eyes on the snaffle.

'Don't go sounding off about the ospreys,' warned Ken. 'Don't go looking for Clare Burnley so you can tell her.'

'Wouldn't matter if the Burnleys knew,' said Jinny, still not looking at Ken. 'They wouldn't harm them. They're not the sort of people who'd go bird nesting.'

'Why? Because they're rich?'

Jinny didn't answer.

'Phew! As if that made any difference. Tell no one. Understand?'

Jinny scrubbed at the green joints of the snaffle. She didn't want to hear what Ken was telling her.

'You can't know what people will do,' Ken insisted. 'So keep your mouth shut, understand?'

'I never said I was going to tell her,' said Jinny.

'Then don't do it,' said Ken, and to Jinny's relief he turned and left her.

When she had put Shantih's tack on she went inside to brush her hair, put on a clean sweater and change her usual messing-about-in anorak for her school one. She rubbed her black lacing school shoes on the sweater she had just taken off and put them on. Then she opened a drawer in her dressing table and took out a pair of yellow string gloves. She looked at them warily. Two years ago they had been a birthday present from an aunt who had heard that Jinny was keen on horses. They were not the sort of thing that Jinny ever thought of wearing. She put them in her pocket. Examining herself in the mirror, Jinny decided that she looked almost respectable. Only her faded, patched jeans looked like herself and since her mother hadn't had time yet to alter Petra's they were all she had, so that was that.

Jinny led Shantih out into the yard and swung herself into the saddle as the Arab plunged up the garden. Checking that no faces were watching from behind the windows, Jinny steered her horse back towards the track to the farm. Shantih raked against the bit, fighting to get her head down and start bucking. Jinny clung tightly onto the saddle. The gentleness of last night was totally forgotten. Like a rubber ball, Shantih bounced and propped from one side of the track to the other.

'Oh stop it,' beseeched Jinny. 'Behave yourself, you idiot.'

But Shantih was wild and uncontrollable. There was no understanding between herself and her rider.

They passed the farm at a flaunting trot, Shantih's hooves clattering faster and faster on the road to Glenbost. Her neck was stretched hard and rigid, her mouth at the end of the reins was an unyielding block of metal. Jinny braced her feet against the stirrups, and tugged with all her strength at the reins, but it only seemed to make Shantih's trot faster and more unbalanced.

What would Ken do? Jinny thought frantically. She knew that she was out of control, that she had no way of slowing Shantih down. A car rattled past them and Shantih panicked forward into a gallop.

Jinny felt the same power surging through her horse as had carried them over the moors in a madness of uncontrollable speed.

Fear lent Jinny strength. She yanked furiously on the reins, jabbing Shantih in the mouth, no thought in her head except to bring Shantih back to a walk. Shantih changed to a trot but her speed scarcely slackened. Her head was almost vertical. Jinny could see the rolling whites of her eyes, her flaring nostrils and her foam-spattered lips.

And I'm doing it to her, Jinny thought. *It's me that's making her like this. She wasn't like this with Ken. Everything I do with her is wrong but I don't know what else to do.* Jinny blinked away tears. Her back and arms ached with pulling against Shantih and her legs had gone slack against the saddle. She was jolted helplessly up and down as Shantih battered on.

I'll need to turn her back home, Jinny thought, knowing that once they reached Glenbost there might be more cars and certainly people to see her and report back to her mother.

Jinny shortened one rein, her hand only inches from Shantih's bit. She kicked with her opposite leg but her heel bounced off the hard wooden surface of Shantih's side. With her head twisted sideways, Shantih continued to trot madly forward.

Jinny saw the track leading to Craigvaar ahead of her.

I'd need to tell Clare there were dinosaurs on the moors to make her speak to me if she saw me now, Jinny thought.

No sooner had the thought come into Jinny's head than she heard the sound of hooves coming from the direction of Craigvaar. Shantih heard them too. She stopped dead, then whinnied with a blast of noise that seemed to reverberate over the moors and hills and bounce back off the mountains.

Jinny felt her stomach freeze and her throat go dry. She knew it must be Clare. In desperation she sawed the reins, drumming her heels against the solid, tense block of Shantih. If she could have turned her, she would have galloped her across the moors to escape from Clare. With terrifying certainty, Jinny knew that once Shantih saw Clare's horse she wouldn't be able to control her. Anything might happen. Jinny clenched her fist and battered it against Shantih's shoulder, shouting at her, kicking her, trying everything she could think of to bring Shantih's attention back to her rider. But it had no effect.

Round the bend in the track came Clare and Spencer Burnley. Clare astride the heavy grey and Spencer on a black thoroughbred. Shantih thundered out a welcome to them. The black horse squealed in reply and Jinny heard the crack of Spencer's stick down the horse's ribs.

The Burnleys trotted down the track, their horses

schooled and obedient. They were talking to each other in loud voices, their faces turned away from Jinny.

'She had this most fantastic little flat,' Clare was saying. '*The* thing for London.' She appeared to be paying no attention to Shantih and Jinny but her hands were strong on the reins and her legs pushed the grey forward. They rode towards Jinny as if she were invisible.

'Well, ask the old man,' said Spencer. 'Got to ask, don't you know.' His black horse tit-upped beside the grey, stretching his long breedy head against the tight standing martingale. 'Could use somewhere like that myself.'

Jinny felt a tremor of excitement go through Shantih as she plunged towards the horses.

'Whoa, whoa, steady, steady, steady,' shouted Jinny, trying to keep her back.

Snorting like a mustang, tail kinked over her back, Shantih pranced beside the Burnleys' horses. Jinny's stirrups crashed against Spencer's. His black horse kicked out peevishly and snaked his head at Shantih. Jinny's mind had gone blank with shame.

'I say, do you mind getting out of my way, there?' demanded Spencer.

Jinny didn't know how to. If she shortened her reins any more she would be holding the bit. She gulped, trying to explain, but only succeeded in making a dry croaking noise.

'That's the same kid that was staring at me the other day,' boomed Clare. 'Would you mind buzzing off? We are trying to go for a ride and we don't particularly want company.'

Jinny went scarlet. Somehow she managed to fight Shantih back two or three strides behind the Burnleys but she could only hold her there for a second. Shantih sank her weight down on to her quarters and reared straight up, then, with a leap like a *capriol*, she had soared through the air and was barging her way between Clare and her brother.

Clare swore, adding something about the value of her horse. Plastered over Shantih's neck, stirrups clattering loosely by Shantih's sides, Jinny couldn't quite hear what it was.

'Oh, enough of this,' said Spencer. 'It really is too much,' and he urged his horse into a canter.

Jinny heard Clare's deep laugh mingling with her brother's high-pitched, 'Yawh, yawh, yawh,' as their horses cantered down the road. She felt herself slipping helplessly to one side and tried to knot her fingers into Shantih's mane but knew that she couldn't stop herself from coming off.

There was a moment when a million hoofs seemed to be crashing down dangerously close to Jinny's head, moments when she was still holding on to Shantih's reins and the tarmac was skimming past under her eyes. Then she was lying in the road watching Clare and her brother galloping along the verge, closely followed by Shantih in a blur of dangling reins, orbiting stirrups and flying hoofs.

Jinny lay for a minute or two before she could pull herself together enough to get up and walk stiffly to the side of the road. The sleeve of her good school anorak was badly torn. Her mother would not be happy about that, she thought. The side of her face was smarting and when Jinny put her hand up to it she discovered it was bleeding. She dipped one of her string gloves into the ditch and wiped her face on it.

The horses were all out of sight and, terrified that they might meet a car or one of the occasional farm tractors, Jinny staggered after them. Her mind had gone numb. She couldn't bear to think about what had happened, but ran head down, her eyes fixed on the road and the school shoes that swung in and out of her vision; shoes that she recognised with surprise as her own each time they appeared.

'Hi,' said Ken.

Jinny stopped running, stood swaying, and managed to lift her head high enough to be able to focus on Ken. He was leading Shantih.

'How did you . . .' began Jinny.

'Here,' said Ken, grasping her by the elbow and guiding her to a rock at the roadside. 'Sit down and get your head between your knees.'

Minutes later Jinny looked up and was relieved to

find that things were standing still again. 'Is Shantih all right?' she asked.

'Fine,' said Ken. 'Slightly soiled by the company she was keeping when I caught her. I was walking into Glenbost when they all came storming down the road.'

'Where are the Burnleys now?' Jinny asked.

'Over the moors and far away,' said Ken. 'Did you go up to Craigvaar?'

'No,' said Jinny, telling the truth but knowing it was a lie. 'They passed me on the road and Shantih would go with them.'

'And they galloped away after you'd fallen off?'

Jinny's mind flipped lightly through the events of the last half hour.

'Don't think they like me much,' she admitted. 'Can't say I blame them. I was making a fool of myself.'

'That's why they galloped off leaving you on the ground? Cool, man, cool. Real nice folks to know. Introduce me sometime.'

'Stop it,' said Jinny, and getting to her feet she took Shantih's reins from Ken and began to lead her home.

It had been foul of the Burnleys to treat her like that, but Jinny knew how mad she got when stupid people kept trailing after her. She saw the Burnleys in her mind's eye riding bright and strong on their well-schooled horses. She didn't blame them for galloping off. She blamed herself for being so feeble.

'Didn't get a chance to tell them about the ospreys then?'

'Sometimes,' said Jinny, 'you are my least favourite person. I wasn't going to tell them.'

'Well don't,' said Ken. 'Just don't.'

Five

Mr Manders phoned up the Royal Society for the Protection of Birds on Monday morning. He had been at Loch Varrich with Petra and Mike and they all felt sure that the ospreys were nesting.

'They were cracking off branches, big bits some of them, and carrying them in their feet to the nest. Took them ages to get them tucked in where they wanted them to go,' said Mike.

Jinny had spent the morning ironing. She was helping her mother to make up for the ruin of her good-school-anorak.

'But why ever did you have your school one on?' her mother had demanded, gazing in dismay at the ragged sleeve. 'It was new at Christmas.'

'When Petra wears her good clothes everything's all right. She's being smart. But when I wear them it's shout, shout, shout. When you've completely spoiled my life I'll need to go to a psychiatrist and he'll understand me.'

'Jinny,' warned her father.

'Let me know when you're going and I'll come too,' said her mother.

'Ride there on Shantih,' suggested Mike. 'Get cheap rates for parties of three.'

'Ha, ha,' said Jinny. 'I'm glad you all find it so funny. I don't find it a bit funny to think that now Shantih belongs to me I don't know enough to school her *and* there's not one of you knows enough to help me.'

'I thought,' said her mother, 'that we were talking about your anorak.'

'I'm *thinking* about Shantih,' Jinny said, and, slamming the door behind her, she had gone upstairs to her bedroom. She had stood at the window, looking down the garden to where Shantih was grazing peacefully with the ponies.

'If you think about it you'll be crying,' Jinny had told herself, and she had found some paper and tried to draw the ospreys. She gave up after two or three unsuccessful attempts and went back, elbows on the windowsill, chin propped on her hands, to stare almost blindly across the garden to the sea, dreaming of how it might have been if only Shantih had behaved herself.

'Two men from the RSPB will be here this afternoon,' Mr Manders now told them, coming off the phone.

'They were thrilled by the news. Osprey sightings have been reported in this area before but this is the first year anyone's reported a nest.'

'Did you tell them that I was first to see it?' Jinny demanded.

'You can tell them yourself,' said Mr Manders.

'Bet Mr MacKenzie knows,' said Mike.

'Mr MacKenzie knows everything,' lamented Jinny. 'When I go for the milk today he'll know everything about me falling off Shantih in front of the Burnleys, he'll know about the ospreys and he'll know that the RSPB men are coming here.'

'How could he possibly?' asked Mrs Manders.

'Well,' said Jinny, 'you'll see.'

The two men from the RSPB arrived at about four o'clock. The one driving their battered Ford van was middle-aged, bearded and peered like a caddis fly from the shell of his duffle hood. Sitting beside him was a young man with a fresh complexion and glasses. He introduced himself as Peter Stevens and his companion as Major Dobbington-Smith – 'known to one and all as Dobbin.' They shook hands with everyone, refused Mrs Manders' offer of tea and, accompanied by Mr Manders, they set off immediately for Loch Varrich.

Jinny went for the milk. She had a bet with herself about which subject Mr MacKenzie would mention first – her violent separation from Shantih or the two strangers with powerful binoculars round their necks.

Jinny decided on Shantih and lost.

'You'll be wanting extra milk for the visitors?' Mr MacKenzie asked her.

'Please,' said Jinny, thinking that no matter what she did these days she was never right. 'Two more pints. I've brought an extra can.'

'They'll be friends of your father's?'

'Yes,' said Jinny.

'Keen on the bird watching?'

'Yes,' said Jinny.

'I was thinking so, seeing them all away up the hill before they'd properly had time to get their feet through the door.'

'Were you?' said Jinny.

Mr MacKenzie spat thoughtfully. 'I was just saying only the other day that you'd all taken a powerful notion to be tramping up to Loch Varrich, and before this you haven't even been saying as much as good morning to the wee loch.'

Jinny said nothing.

'You'll have chiselled out the sea eagle I'm thinking,' said Mr MacKenzie, pouring out Jinny's milk.

'I knew you'd know,' exclaimed Jinny.

'Aye,' agreed Mr MacKenzie. 'There's not much moves on the hill but I have my eye to it.'

'Well, one of your Shetlands had a great lump of wire caught up in her tail about three weeks ago, and Mike and I caught her and pulled it out. She nearly kicked Mike's face in.'

'Och, I knew it fine. I don't trust them an inch myself. I was hoping you would notice it. I knew if you spotted it you wouldn't be resting until you'd the whole business sorted out. I daresay it was yourself that spotted the sea eagle?'

'If you must know,' said Jinny, 'yes it was. And the two men are from the RSPB.'

'Is that a fact you're telling me? I'd never have guessed it, and them looking like American tourists with their cameras and their fancy glasses.'

'Do the ospreys always nest there?'

'In the old days, yes. Then it was the gentry like yourselves were for shooting them for taking the trout out of the loch. But the past year or two now they've made a go at the nesting again, and not a soul but myself knowing. Last year did they not manage it with the one wee one? So I'm hoping all your nonsense will not drive them away this year.'

''Course not,' said Jinny. 'We're trying to protect them.'

'Leave well alone,' suggested Mr MacKenzie.

'That's more or less what Ken said.'

'Aye, he's not such a dooley as he looks, that one.' Mr MacKenzie lowered his head and looked at Jinny out of the corner of one pink-rimmed eye socket. 'He's more fit for that mare than yourself, that's for sure.'

'I suppose you know all about that too?'

79

'Straight from Clare Burnley's own mouth. Asking me who this girl was with the fancy horse and not able to stay on its back for two seconds together.'

'I daresay you told her,' said Jinny, picking up the milk cans.

'Indeed yes. I said we were acquainted. I'm thinking she'll be a bit lonely with her brother going off with his friends and leaving her here alone. Looking for a friend herself, I shouldn't wonder.'

'Won't be me,' Jinny told him and set off back to Finmory.

It was nearly dark by the time Dobbin, Peter and Mr Manders got back.

'Not a doubt. They're nesting all right,' said Dobbin, standing in front of the drawing room fire. 'What a piece of luck. What an afternoon. And you're the young lady who saw them first?'

Jinny said she was.

'Good. Good. Now the thing is to keep it secret. Not a word. Not a word from any of us,' and he looked round them all, his glare resting slightly longer on Ken's long hair than it did on the others. 'Clear on that? Good. Good. Pity you used the phone this morning. Never know who might overhear. In the early days at Loch Garten they sent telegrams to each other by code. Military operation. That's how we look at it. Trust no one. Even a duke may have an egg collector lurking under his skin. Can't judge from the outside.

Now, let's get down to brass tacks, get the details worked out.'

Mrs Manders suggested that before the details were planned they should all have supper.

When they had eaten, they all sat round the kitchen table and worked out a plan of campaign, as Dobbin called it.

Jinny told them that Mr MacKenzie knew about the nest and that the ospreys had reared one chick last year.

'Good. Good,' said Dobbin. 'That means the locals aren't in the habit of popping up to the loch for a picnic, or someone would have spotted them last year and we'd have heard about them.'

'You hardly ever see anyone on the moors,' said Jinny.

'Good. Good,' said Dobbin, and Peter said it only took one person to ruin the birds' chances and that the sooner they got a guard rota worked out the sooner he'd be pleased.

'Right away,' said Dobbin. 'She'll probably start laying tomorrow or the next day. Usually lay three eggs. Hatch out in about five weeks. Once the first egg is laid, until they hatch – that's the danger time. Got to man a watch day and night. Mrs Manders, ma'am, do you think you could put up with two of our fellows bunking down here for the next month or so?'

Mrs Manders said that as long as they had their

own sleeping bags they would be most welcome.

'Good. Good,' said Dobbin, and began to draw a grid on a large sheet of paper. 'Guard duties,' he announced. 'Know you young people will be bursting at the seams, longing to help.'

Jinny regarded the mesh of lines with suspicion. It looked dangerously like a timetable to her.

'I have my horse to ride,' she said, glaring round at her family, challenging them to make any remarks about her riding.

'Fit that in,' Dobbin assured her, ruling his lines. 'Two chaps on at night. One during the day. How about you kids taking over some of the daytime watches? Fit you up with a walkie-talkie. See any signs of a stranger, contact base and reinforcements will be over at the double.'

'Doubt if any egg collector would risk it during the day,' said Peter. 'Not now it's illegal.'

'One good thing,' said Mrs Manders, 'is the openness of the site. You can spot anyone approaching for miles around.'

'True,' said Peter. 'Definite advantage.'

When the duty roster, as Dobbin called his timetable, was filled in, Jinny's first spell of duty was in two days' time.

I'll need to exercise Shantih tomorrow, Jinny thought. Coiled at the back of her mind was the knowledge that she hadn't ridden her today.

I didn't have time, Jinny thought, but she knew that if she had really wanted to ride she could have made time in the afternoon. *It's just that I don't want to go on making her more disobedient. And that's all I'm doing. Worse and worst and worstest. Why can't I just explain to her that once she stops being so silly then we can both start to enjoy ourselves? Maybe she thinks it's me that's silly. Maybe she wants me to understand and let her run wild with the Shetlands again.*

But Jinny didn't believe that. When she called from her bedroom window, Shantih would look up from her grazing and whinny, knowing her; or she would come trotting gladly to the field gate. It was only when Jinny was riding her that things went wrong.

Dobbin and Peter, who were both staying for the night and going out to the hide at dawn, went to bed early. Dobbin had to be back at business the next day, but Peter, who worked for the RSPB was to stay and be joined by another helper.

Going to bed, Jinny thought about the ospreys, out in the night at that very minute, exposed and vulnerable. She thought of the egg collectors who had overheard her father's phone call speeding through the darkness in powerful Dick Dastardly cars, all converging on Finmory, waiting to pounce the minute the eggs were laid. What had Ken said? Something about not thinking, when you saw a hawk, that you ought to do things for it. But protecting it was different, protecting it while it hatched out its eggs, so that soon there would be ospreys again in Scotland and lots of other people would be able to see what she and Ken had seen – the sudden crystal bloom when the osprey shook its feathers dry, and its soaring, effortless mastery of space.

The next morning when Jinny brought Shantih in she could feel at once that her horse was in a good mood. She stood still while Jinny groomed her, lowered her head for the bit and hardly blew herself out at all when Jinny was tightening her girth. Jinny led her out of the stable and quickly sprang up into the saddle. Shantih turned her head, mild-eyed, looking round at Jinny.

'Don't you look like that,' Jinny told her. 'You know as well as I do that you're not always like this.'

Shantih nibbled at the toe of Jinny's shoe, then waited quietly for her rider to tell her where to go. Jinny wondered whether she should go to the field and try once more to make Shantih walk and trot in a circle. For a moment she was undecided.

'Oh, fiddle it,' Jinny said aloud. 'It's too nice a day to start fighting with you. We'll go down to the beach,' and Jinny lightly touched Shantih forward.

She walked out with a neat step. When Shantih was in a mood like this everything about her was sharp and exact, even her mane, spiked out by the sea breeze, seemed to form a rhythmical pattern with the swing of her shoulders and the arch of her neck.

'*Morning has broken like the first morning. Morning has broken like the first day*,' sang Jinny tunelessly.

The tide was out and the sand firm and printless. Jinny let Shantih trot the length of the bay, then cantered her back. Shantih only bucked once, and then it was more kicking her heels in the air for fun rather than bucking. Jinny walked her about and then trotted. The calm sea glinted kaleidoscope lozenges of light, gulls screamed through the blue spring air and Jinny felt floating with happiness that Shantih was going so well.

'I say, you jolly well ought not to trot them on wet sand. Terribly bad for their tendons.'

Clare Burnley on her black horse was coming towards them. With Clare riding him, the horse looked weedier than he had done with Spencer. Clare's solid bulk pressed the lightness out of him, took away the sparkle.

Jinny's mouth dropped open with sheer surprise. Amazing enough that Clare Burnley should appear at Finmory Bay, but even more incredible that she should be standing there chatting.

'I came over to see if you were still in one piece after yesterday's disaster. We were just going to bring your horse back to you when this boy appeared from nowhere and grabbed her.'

Jinny's mouth cracked down another notch at such

an obvious lie. She didn't think Clare or Spencer had shown the least sign of caring what happened to Shantih or herself.

'I've been talking to old MacKenzie about you, and he told me about your horse. Pretty tremendous – rescuing her from a circus and saving her life. I expect you are jolly proud of it all.'

Jinny had never thought of it like that. It had been love, not pride, that had made her fight on and on to save Shantih.

'And he showed me the paintings you did for him. They're absolutely something. I could hardly believe you could have done them. I mean to say you'd think a real artist had painted them. It would be super if you could come over to Craigvaar some day and draw my nags for me. Mr MacKenzie says you're crazy about horses, so I expect you'd enjoy having a look round the tack room and seeing some of my rosettes and things. Of course, they are only the ones I've picked up in Scotland. All my cups are kept at home. Wouldn't be safe leaving them up here when we're in Sussex. As Pa says, no point in inviting the locals to break into Craigvaar.'

Words thundered out of Clare like a waterfall.

'I mean, imagine what it would be like if we had word in the middle of winter that Craigvaar had been broken into. The bore of having to come buzzing up here. I couldn't abide being up here in the winter. Ma says it's only families like the MacKenzies who have never known anything else who could put up with it. I mean think of the parties one would miss. Let's face it, winter is the time when everything happens in town. You're stuck up here all the year, aren't you? But then I don't suppose you're old enough to bother much about parties and shows and things.'

Jinny had managed to get her mouth shut again. She sat on Shantih mesmerised by Clare's presence. She could not believe that Clare was spending time talking to her, that she actually seemed to have come looking for her.

Clare's short blonde hair curled round the edges of her hard hat. It was a new hat – still dense, velvety black. Her blue tweed jacket and fawn jodhpurs were made of thick, expensive material and her black jodhpur boots were highly polished. Her thoroughbred twitched his silk-fine hide as he waited motionless. His tack was dark and mellowed, better than new. Clare sat solidly in the saddle. She rode with long stirrups, her feet pushed well home. Her hands were moulded round the reins like lumps of Mr Manders' clay.

'Your mare's a bit on the skinny side,' said Clare. 'How old is she?'

'I'm not sure,' said Jinny. 'About six, we think.'

"We" meant herself and Mike and Jinny's pony book with the diagram of horses' teeth in it. Had anyone else suggested that Shantih was skinny Jinny would have exploded in their face, but somehow Clare Burnley was different. She knew about horses. She was allowed to criticise.

'Just a youngster then. That's why she's so green. Do her good to be ridden with other horses.'

'I ride her with our Highlands,' Jinny said, making it sound as if Bramble and Punch were their own ponies and not borrowed trekkers.

'Oh, I mean other *horses*,' said Clare. 'Goodness, I'd think it would bore the pants off her having those two mini carthorses keeping her back all the time.'

Jinny was very fond of Bramble – his tough independence, his native sureness on the moors, but at Clare's words Jinny's idea of Bramble seemed to change. Somehow he became something to be ashamed of. Not the sort of animal Clare would have in her stable.

'Gosh, would you look at the time! I'll need to dash. Ma and I are going over to see our little man this afternoon. Does the most wonderful weaving. Really pretty. The sort of thing you could not buy in London.'

Clare turned the black thoroughbred with confident dominance. He looked almost seventeen hands, hard-muscled and fit, but Clare made him seem like a child's pony.

'And you will come over, won't you? Ma would adore to meet you. I'll come and pick you up in the car if you like.'

The sea wind fanned Clare's words out into space so that when she had ridden out of sight Jinny couldn't be certain that she had really said them. Perhaps she had said something quite different. If it hadn't been for the hoofprints in the sand, Jinny would have been willing to believe that she had dreamed it all.

Jinny walked Shantih along the crimpling edge of the waves. She was too happy to go home yet. She wanted to keep the warm, fizzy happiness bottled up inside her for a bit longer. Riding back to Finmory she was still sealed inside the golden bubble. She hardly saw the mountains or the sky. Clare Burnley had really and truly stood talking to her.

'Just as if I was her friend,' Jinny said aloud to Shantih.

'Don't be too disappointed if you don't hear any more from her,' Mrs Manders said after Jinny had told her about their meeting. 'She is a good bit older than you.'

'Oh, Ma!' exclaimed Jinny. 'Don't be such a bore. She's coming for me in their car. She said.'

'Shouldn't it be, "calling for me in the Bentley?"' asked Ken.

$\mathcal{S}ix$

Brian Craven, the other man from the RSPB, arrived that evening with his sleeping bag wrapped in polythene and strapped to the back of his scooter. He was small and wiry and worried a lot about pollution.

'You feel that no matter how much you do, it can't be enough. What can I do against all the factories that are churning out their muck, all the nice, kind, ignorant idiots pressing their filthy aerosol cans, the murderers spreading their chemical poisons everywhere?' he demanded, and sank his head into his hands, narrowly missing the plate of broth that Mrs Manders had just put down on the table for him. 'Still, the ospreys haven't given up, so why should I? When am I going to see them?' and he began to gulp down his soup.

'We do the night watch,' Peter told him. 'Dobbin

worked it all out before he left. Then Ken comes up early morning and one of the kids changes with him at about eleven.'

'Two of us,' corrected Mike. 'Dobbin thought that since it was our first time at the hide, Jinny and I should go together.'

'Don't see why it needs you both,' said Petra. 'I was there by myself.' Petra had acquired a notebook and was keeping a careful record of every move the ospreys made while she was on watch.

'Mike can go by himself if he wants to,' offered Jinny quickly. She was haunted by the fear that while she was in the hide Clare might arrive to take her to Craigvaar.

'Don't spoil it,' said Mike. 'It's all arranged. We're going together.'

I'll die, thought Jinny. *I will, I'll die if Clare come for me and I'm stuck up on the moors.*

'Couldn't you phone her?' Mrs Manders had suggested. 'Let her know you can't go tomorrow.'

'No, of course I can't. She may have meant next week or she may have forgotten all about me by now,' Jinny had snapped.

She hugged the terrible fear to herself that if Clare did come and Jinny was watching the nest she wouldn't bother to come again. Jinny would have missed her chance of getting to know someone who could help her school Shantih.

At breakfast, Brian and Peter were full of enthusiasm for their night's watching.

'She's probably laid her first egg,' said Peter. 'We think she's beginning to brood.'

'Nearly certain,' agreed Brian. 'For the next five weeks it's Red Alert.'

Through the window Jinny could see white scuds of cloud racing over blue sky, their moving shadows patching the sunlight on the kitchen floor.

I don't care about the ospreys, she thought rebelliously, but she did really. She wanted to do all she could to make sure that the great birds should be allowed to rear their young without being disturbed. It was just that she cared more about Shantih, about finding someone who could tell her what she was doing wrong. She had been up early that morning, riding Shantih in the field and had been bucked off twice.

'Come on, Jinny,' Mike yelled from the bottom of the stairs. 'It's a quarter to eleven and we're meant to be at the hide to let Ken away at eleven.'

There's no chance of that, thought Jinny sullenly. She had been waiting as long as she dared, praying for the sound of the Burnleys' car coming up the drive.

'The rota will be all mucked up if you don't come now,' shouted Mike. Jinny made a face at herself in the mirror and stomped reluctantly downstairs.

'Fiddle his stupid old timetable,' she said. 'Thought we were meant to be on holiday.'

'You wouldn't say that if you were Ken waiting for us to arrive at eleven and we're not even going to be there for half past.'

Mike was already mounted on Punch. They would share the pony on their way to the hide and Ken would ride him back. Jinny took a last hopeful look down the drive, a last listen for the least sound that might be the Burnleys' car, but there was nothing. She turned and ran to catch up with Punch and Mike.

She pushed the thought of Clare out of her mind. *Maybe she didn't mean it*, Jinny thought as she walked beside Punch.

'Can you believe that we ever lived in Stopton?' Mike asked.

Jinny shook her head.

'That this is us going to guard ospreys?'

'Can't,' said Jinny. 'Can't.'

She swung her arms wide through the open space, spinning round, blinding herself with her hair. They were so lucky to be themselves. So much had happened since they'd come to Finmory.

Jinny stopped and looked back at the house. Parked at the front door was the Burnleys' car.

'She's come,' Jinny screamed. She saw Clare get out of the car, her curls bright in the sun. 'Clare's come for me and I'm not there!'

'Dad'll tell her to come back tomorrow. It doesn't matter.'

'Of course it does,' raged Jinny. 'She may never come back. Never. Shantih won't have a chance to be properly schooled.' Clear in her mind's eye Jinny saw Clare standing in the centre of the schooling circle, correcting Jinny's faults as she rode round on Shantih. 'I've got to go with her!'

'You can't,' said Mike. Mrs Manders had come out of the house and was talking to Clare. 'She'll have gone long before you could get back down.'

'Let me have Punch,' demanded Jinny and for a moment she thought of trying to drag Mike off the pony.

'Don't be daft,' Mike said, kicking Punch on up the moor. 'Ken's waiting for us.'

Jinny made no move to follow him. She stood staring down to where her mother and Clare were still standing talking. She knew it was true that she could never reach Finmory in time. Jinny glared round furiously. There must be some way. The roof of Mr MacKenzie's farm caught her eye and instantly she was tearing full speed over the moor towards it. Clare might stop there on her way home.

Jinny sprang and leapt from tussocks of reeds to rock face to heather. She hurtled down to the farm, throwing herself on faster and faster, never glancing down to see where her feet would go next. She gasped for breath, sucking in air that burned like drinking cold water after curry. Her heart shook her body with its jumping but she forced herself on until at last she staggered into the farmyard and saw the Burnleys' car with Clare leaning out of the window talking to Mr MacKenzie.

'Well, hello!' cried Clare. 'However did you get here? Anything wrong?'

'Saw . . . your . . . car.' Between words Jinny stopped and gulped for breath. 'Was running . . . to catch . . . you.'

'Your Ma said you'd gone for a ride in the hills and there wasn't the remotest chance of your being back before the evening. She made it quite clear that there was absolutely no point in my hanging around.'

'Changed . . . my mind.'

'It's the hard time that mother of yours has trying to keep tabs on you,' said Mr MacKenzie.

'She knew,' said Jinny, still too breathless to even begin to argue. 'I just changed my mind.'

'Jolly glad you did,' boomed Clare. 'Ma wants you to come over for lunch. Actually she's expecting you. I mean to say I knew you were keen to see the horses so I really more or less said you would be coming. She'll be frightfully put out if you don't.'

'Oh, yes please,' said Jinny.

'Do you want to tell them at home? Go back and change or anything like that?'

'It's OK. They'll know where I've gone.'

'Just as you like,' said Clare.

It wasn't really as Jinny liked. She knew from the expression on Clare's face that she didn't think much of her appearance. Jinny glanced down at her splashed jeans and muddy wellingtons. Under her old anorak she was wearing a heavy sweater that had once belonged to Petra. It reached to her knees but had been meant to keep her warm in the hide. Jinny quite understood that she wasn't at all the kind of guest Mrs Burnley would be expecting to arrive for lunch but she was afraid that if she went back home to clean herself up she would be re-routed back to Mike.

'At least be having the decency to take the moor off your boots before you get into the posh car,' said Mr MacKenzie.

Jinny sluiced water from the trough over her wellingtons.

'But what a bore for you,' said Clare. 'Don't be too particular. We'll be out in the stables most of the time and I can easily lend you a pair of slippers to wear when we go in for lunch.'

Mr MacKenzie fixed Jinny with his gimlet eye. 'Be minding your manners and keep a good hold on your tongue. Don't be shaming me now in front of my friends.'

'Phooey,' said Jinny, and dived into the car next to Clare.

'We all think he's a perfectly sweet old man,' said Clare as they drove to Craigvaar. 'Perfectly sweet.'

It was not the word Jinny would have picked to describe Mr MacKenzie.

Clare drove up the drive and parked in front of Craigvaar.

'Now I'll tell Ma we've arrived and then should we go down to the stables? Would that be the thing?'

Jinny was left standing uncertainly beside the car. She looked round cautiously at the bowling green lawns and their controlled flowerbeds; the gravelled drive marching between ankle-high posts and chains and the two stone lions guarding the doorway.

'Ma is jolly pleased you've come,' said Clare, emerging, 'but she says will you excuse her if she doesn't come out to say hello just now? We do have Pat and Heather to help us, but Ma's so fussy about the cooking she just has to be there to see to it herself. So I thought if it was all right with you we'd trot down now to see the nags and maybe ride this afternoon? How would that be?'

'Oh, yes,' said Jinny, just managing to stop herself blurting out her utter surprise that Clare should even think of letting her ride one of her horses.

They went round the side of the house, over lawns bounded on one side by a tennis court and through a shrubbery until they came to the stables. There were four loose boxes. The horses, hearing them coming, were looking out expectantly over their half doors.

'Gee back,' Clare shouted at the grey, swinging her

arm at him and making him plunge and swing back into his box. She opened the door and Jinny followed her in.

Inside, the grey seemed even more massive than he had outside. His shoulders and quarters bulged with muscle from his round, deep-ribbed body. He carried his broad, Roman-nosed face on a thick-set neck. He was a horse made to pack into a cube or as if he were not quite free of the stone block from which he had been carved.

'Meet Huston,' said Clare. 'I've only had him for a year. Pa bought him for me to get me going in the open jumping. He was absolutely wonderful for that. I won dozens of comps on him last summer but he is rather slow so one hardly knows what to do about keeping him. Of course, what I would really like is a top class event horse, but they cost thousands these days.'

Jinny clapped Huston's neck and the flat, impersonal expanse of cheek bone but he paid no attention to her.

'He looks as if he'd be a good hunter,' Jinny said because she thought it would sound the right thing.

'Oh goodness no, far too slow.'

They left the mountain of Huston standing carved in the middle of his box and went to see the black horse.

'We'll not go in,' said Clare. 'Jasper is rather spooky. Quiet as a lamb with me but he is inclined to have a go at a stranger. Mind you, he is a super horse. I should say he's won more cups for showing than almost any other horse one could name. Of course, I do take him around a bit and now I can drive the horsebox myself it does make a tremendous difference.'

Jasper made a grab at Clare's arm, ears pinned down on his blue-black reptilian head.

'Don't you dare,' roared Clare. 'Or I'll be in there with my big stick.'

The black horse gloomed away from Clare's voice. He stood in the far corner of his box, kicking boredly with a hind leg. His coat shimmered like black ice.

'You must spend hours grooming him,' said Jinny knowing how long it took her to polish up Shantih.

'Gosh no,' laughed Clare. 'I plug in my brushes. Electric groomers. Don't tell me you haven't heard of them?'

Jinny decided not to say that she enjoyed grooming Shantih. Standing beside Clare it did seem stupid to enjoy work when a machine could do it for you.

'Now the tack room,' said Clare, marching down the row of boxes and opening another door at the end of them.

They stayed in the tack room until lunchtime, Clare pointing out different rosettes that were pinned round the walls and telling Jinny how she had won them.

Lunch was fish pie, eaten by Jinny with a knife and fork but by the Burnleys with a fork only, and a dessert of fruit, which was a bowl of apples and pears. Jinny picked an apple and took a bite out of it. The Burnleys laid theirs on their plates and cut them into small pieces, but to Jinny's relief they didn't seem to notice her. In fact they hardly seemed to notice that she was there at all. After Mrs Burnley had shaken hands and said what wonderfully pretty hair Jinny had and Mr Burnley had said, 'Manders? Manders? Don't think I know your father,' no one said another word to Jinny. They sat and talked to each other about people they knew who all seemed to have been doing wonderful, fascinating things.

'Now, darlings, what have you planned for this afternoon?' Mrs Burnley asked when Pat had cleared the table.

'We're riding,' said Clare.

Mrs Burnley said that if they were going to ride she did think that perhaps they should go now because she had promised Dinkie Clifton that they would all be over for drinks before supper.

'Can you tack up Huston?' Clare asked.

Jinny thought she could and Clare handed her his tack.

The huge grey stood perfectly still, only his ears twitching as Clare bawled at Jasper. Jinny felt as if she was saddling up a house – he was so huge compared to Shantih. His legs were like pillars, his back like a table top and Jinny had to march round him to get from one side to the other.

'Jolly well done,' said Clare, crashing her hand down on the saddle to make sure it was sitting correctly on Huston's back, and checking the tightness of his throat lash. 'Now will you ride this fellow and I'll take Jasper?'

Jinny nodded. She was too excited to trust her voice.

'Wellingtons are not the thing for riding but I'm afraid my boots would drown you. But I can lend you a hat. One always feels it is so important to get into the habit of never riding without a hard hat. It was Ma's idea to keep one or two old ones up here so I can usually kit out my friends. Come along and we'll find one for you.'

The third hat Jinny tried on fitted her.

'Keep it well down,' said Clare, banging it more firmly on to Jinny's head. 'And here's a stick. One should never ride without a stick. Don't you agree? Must say that squib of yours could have done with one across her ribs the way she was carrying on when we met you.'

Jinny said nothing. She didn't feel it was the right time to start explaining why she never used a stick on Shantih.

Clare gave Jinny a leg up onto the grey, chucking her high above the saddle, so that she nearly went flying over the other side.

'Thought we'd go for a hack first and then back to the paddock,' Clare said when she was sitting astride Jasper, and she led the way out of Craigvaar.

Once on the road the horses settled into a steady jog. In minutes they seemed to be through Glenbost and trotting along the road to Ardtallon. The most Jinny could do was to keep her mouth shut. She couldn't stop it grinning. She had never known riding like this before, so controlled and effortless. Huston seemed to be so powerful and yet was obedient to the least tightening of Jinny's fingers on the reins, the least touch of her leg against his side.

'How do you like him?' asked Clare.

'He's super,' said Jinny.

'He's pretty well schooled, I'll say that for him, and he is fit. Barbara, our girl at home, is an absolute wonder at feeding horses. I expect you notice the difference after your beast. Really, I'd be rather ashamed to be seen out on her.'

'She's too fresh as she is. I can't give her any more oats.'

'Oh, feeding isn't just a question of shovelling in oats. You have to know what you're doing.'

And Jinny thought as they rode on that it all came back to the same thing: she didn't know anything. *If only my family were like Clare's*, she thought. *If only I knew as much as she does.*

'I'll tuck this fellow away in his box,' Clare said when they were back in the stable yard, 'and then we'll take Huston into the paddock and give him a jump.'

In one corner of the paddock were five jumps built

out of smart red and white poles, all standing at about three feet.

'D'you want a jolly round them?'

Jinny swallowed hard. She couldn't bring herself to tell Clare that she had never jumped before.

'OK,' she said.

'Canter him round a few times, then over you go when you're ready. He's got a big leap in him, so watch out for it, but I'll guarantee he won't stop.'

Jinny cantered Huston round the field. He had a slow, comfortable, rocking-horse canter and Jinny was able to sit down tight in the saddle. She shortened her reins and rode at the first jump, trying to remember all she had ever read about jumping.

'Lean forward when he takes off, keep your knees tight and your heels down and don't catch his mouth,' she told herself. But all she was actually thinking about was that she was riding one of Clare Burnley's horses, and that she was learning to jump in Clare Burnley's paddock.

Huston cantered steadily at the first jump, cleared it effortlessly, landed heavily on the far side and they were cantering towards the second almost before Jinny realised that they had left the ground.

With the same easy confidence Huston cleared the first four jumps. Jinny turned him up the middle and felt him gather speed for the last one. Yards in front of the poles he shot into the air, sailed high above them and stretched himself to land far out over the other side. Just in time Jinny jack-knifed over his shoulder, dug her knees tightly into the rolls of the saddle and let the reins slip through her fingers. In a stride or two Huston had come back to a walk.

'He went well for you,' boomed Clare, striding towards them. 'Glad to see you'd enough sense not to interfere with him. When a horse knows about jumping the way he knows about it, one is best to leave him alone. I mean to say that when Pa picked him he picked a horse that was going to teach me to sit on over decent-sized fences.'

'That was wonderful,' enthused Jinny. 'It was super. He just flew over them. Oh, if only Shantih could jump like that,' and Jinny was sailing over Clare Burnley's jumps on Shantih, her horse as confident as Huston but twice as fast.

'Bring her down and give her a school over them,' offered Clare, as if she was suggesting that Jinny should have another piece of cake.

'Oh, but I couldn't. I can't even lunge her properly. I could never start jumping her.'

'Nothing to lungeing. Let them know who's the boss, that's all. I've been lungeing my own ponies since I was about seven, I suppose.'

'Clare,' called Mrs Burnley's voice. 'Phone.'

'Wonder who?' said Clare. 'Hang on here a tick.'

She ran into the house, leaving Jinny to walk Huston

round the paddock. She looked longingly at the jumps, aching to go round them again but she was too afraid that Clare might return and order her home.

'I say, I'm frightfully sorry dashing off like that,' said Clare, when she came back a few minutes later. 'That was Tim Foster, terribly nice chap, didn't realise we were here. He's coming over in an hour or so. Would it be a bore if I were to drive you home now? I know what Tim's like once he starts talking and we are going out for drinks this evening. Would you be awfully offended?'

'No. That's OK,' Jinny said, and in no time Huston was packed back in his box and Jinny was sitting next to Clare being driven back to Finmory.

'I'll drop you here,' said Clare, stopping at Finmory's gates. 'It has been wonderful getting to know you like this.'

'I've had a smashing day,' said Jinny, getting out of the car. 'Thank you very, very much.'

'I say, you didn't really mean it, about not being able to lunge your nag?'

'I did. She just plays about with me.'

'Well, the thing is,' said Clare, 'why don't you bring her over to Craigvaar and I could sort you out a bit?'

'Oh, but . . . would you? Would you really?'

'I'll bring the box over for her. Tomorrow's no use. Bobs and Bunty are with us for the day. How about Friday? Well, that's it definitely arranged. No point in me slaving away looking after two horses by myself when we could cope with them together.'

Clare turned the car and drove away. Jinny vaulted over the gate, went leaping and running up the drive, burst into the house and through the hall to the kitchen. Her mother, Mike and Peter were sitting round the table drinking tea.

'I'm going to Craigvaar,' she shouted. 'Clare's bringing her horsebox for Shantih and she's going to teach me how to lunge her. And I rode one of her horses. And I jumped!'

Jinny flung herself round the kitchen, stamping her wellingtons, shaking her hair and waving her arms.

'Big deal,' said Mike, and Jinny remembered about the ospreys.

$\mathcal{S}$*even*

Jinny's alarm clock woke her into the cold grey light of very early morning. She stretched out one arm to switch off its hideous disturbance then remembered that last night she had left it on the other side of her room so that she couldn't switch it off and go back to sleep. Jinny muffled the noise by curling under the bedclothes, but by the time it had exhausted itself she was wide enough awake to know that she had to get up. To make up for yesterday's desertion, Jinny had agreed to take the early morning watch at the ospreys' nest.

After her first mug of coffee she felt a little better.

'It's a drug,' said Ken, coming into the kitchen with Kelly shadowing his heels.

'Don't care,' said Jinny making herself a second mugful. 'Why are you up so early?'

'Thought I'd walk up the moor a bit with you,' said

Ken. 'I'm looking for some plants for my compost. My book says they should be picked before the sun has been on them.'

'Not much danger of that,' said Jinny, looking out at the grey gloom.

Ken walked, Jinny rode Bramble. She was pretending that Ken wasn't there. Last night when they had all been telling her what they thought about her for spending the day at Craigvaar, Ken hadn't said anything. Jinny felt that this was why he was with her now.

'You're not really taking Shantih over to the Burnleys'?' asked Ken, so that Jinny knew she'd been right.

'Am,' she said.

'Forget it,' said Ken. 'She doesn't want you.'

'Clare does. She asked me to come.'

'Because her brother's away and she's bored hairless.'

'She's going to teach me how to lunge.'

'Is that what she was doing when she rode off and left you lying on the road?'

'She didn't mean to.'

'Didn't notice you'd fallen off?'

Jinny ignored his sarcasm. 'Clare's sending her horsebox for Shantih tomorrow and I'm going over to Craigvaar as well. And if you'd like to know, I might be going with them to Inverburgh Show.'

'Don't do it,' said Ken. He clicked his bony fingers

together, a sharp sound in the pearly silence. 'Stop now,' he commanded. 'Don't go on with it. Great what you've got here. Enjoy it. Live this and don't go complicating it all.'

Jinny blocked herself off from him. She thought hard about Huston, the excitement of jumping, the luxury of Clare's tack room. She didn't care what Ken said – she was taking Shantih to Craigvaar. She glanced down at him and he looked straight at her, his eyes flint hard.

'You don't need to go on,' Ken said. 'I'm giving you the chance to get off. Tell Clare Burnley you're not playing her game.'

'Honestly,' said Jinny, 'one wonders what all the fuss is about.'

'Well if you must, you must,' said Ken, and Jinny knew he had totally abandoned herself, Shantih and everything to do with Craigvaar. It was as if he had been shining a torch directly at her face but now he had switched it off.

'I'd better get a move on,' Jinny said, to break the silence. 'They'll be expecting me.'

Ken nodded and Jinny pushed Bramble into a trot.

Peter and Brian were stiff and cold after their night of watching.

'All's well,' Brian said. 'She's been brooding all night and he's off fishing at the moment. May have gone down to the sea.'

He gave Jinny the binoculars. She looked through them and exclaimed with surprise. Although the hide was in a cave on the hillside and Loch Varrich lay in the hollow a good distance from the hills, Jinny could see every blade of grass by the lochside and each smooth tiny pebble. The glasses were far more powerful than her father's.

Jinny found the mass of branches and twigs, high in the pine tree, that was the osprey's nest. The hen osprey seemed so close that Jinny could see every detail of her black, hooked beak, the crest of feathers lying flat on her head and her great yellow eye that seemed to be staring straight at the hide.

'You got her?' Peter asked, breaking the spell.

'Cor!' breathed Jinny, taking the glasses away from her eyes and seeing the nest as a hardly visible shape. 'They are terrific glasses. Oh, I should love to have a pair like these all the time!'

'They're Dobbin's,' said Brian. 'Don't think we could afford them.'

Before they went, Brian and Peter showed Jinny how to operate the walkie-talkie. As well as watching for any disturbance at the nest, she was to scan the hills sloping down to the loch, and contact Finmory should she see anyone at all.

'Petra's coming to relieve you about eleven,' said Brian. 'Now no dozing off. You have to concentrate all the time you're on duty up here.'

'And no nipping off to see your friends,' warned Peter.

Jinny scowled at him. It was bad enough having her own family telling her what to do without a complete stranger bossing her about as well.

Left alone, Jinny settled herself down. She arranged the cushion on top of the wooden box as comfortably as she could. Then she sat with her elbows on her knees, the glasses to her eyes.

Daylight stretched over the sky, colours dyeing the grey hillside to life. Jinny's arm ached and her legs were cramped but she stayed still, her glasses trained on the hen osprey who never moved either, seeming almost a part of the nest.

The cock osprey came flying towards the pines, carrying a fish in his talons. For a second, the balance of the hills and the loch changed. Everything drew in its breath to a moment of stillness, the focus held in the wings of the hawk.

The hen stood up in the nest, chuckling to her mate, took the fish from him and flew with it to the topmost branch of a neighbouring pine where she began to eat it. The male stood for a minute, glaring around him, then he settled down over the eggs.

Hardly daring to blink, Jinny stared, magnetised by the wonder of it. Yet she felt cold and squirmy at the same time. She was an intruder prying into the private lives of the ospreys. She had no right to be staring at them so rudely. Shivering, Jinny wondered if God might be staring down at her without her knowing anything about it.

When the hen had eaten the fish she came back to the nest and the cock flapped to a high branch where he sat motionless.

Jinny took a pad of drawing paper and a pencil out of her pocket. Quickly, almost guiltily, she sketched the osprey. Her pencil sweeping in the line of the hawk's flight, the strength of its talons and the reflector scan of its fierce yellow eyes. She had drawn several pictures of the ospreys – the male flying, sitting on the edge of the nest and brooding, motionless, almost like a branch of the pine, and two of the female tucked into the nest – and was just beginning to draw the osprey diving on the fish when she suddenly remembered that she was meant to be on guard.

Quickly Jinny looked round the hillside, but as usual there were only sheep to be seen.

Thank goodness for that, she thought. *After yesterday, if I'd let anything happen to the eggs I think they'd have murdered me.*

Petra arrived riding Punch and said she was sorry she was late. Jinny said it was OK because she didn't know the time, and Petra said how could she take accurate notes about the ospreys' behaviour if she didn't know the time. Jinny said it did make things difficult, and escaped on Punch.

She got back to Finmory as her father was loading crates of pottery into the car to take in to Inverburgh to the gift shop that bought it from him.

'Take Jinny with you, seeing Ken's not going,' suggested Mrs Manders. 'There's a sale on at Smythe & Binns. Girls' anoraks for three pounds. If they're worth having you could buy one for her. She'll need to get a new one for school.'

'But I'm going to ride Shantih,' protested Jinny. 'Couldn't Daddy just buy one that's my size?'

'No,' said Mrs Manders, 'he could not.'

Jinny decided not to argue. She could do with a new anorak, then if she went to the Inverburgh Show with Clare she would be able to wear it.

Mr Manders parked in a side street close to the gift shop and Jinny helped him to carry in the crates of pottery.

'Joy, joy, joy!' cried Nell Storr, who owned the shop. 'Delight to see you, to see you – delight! Sold out of your last lot, and I've got a special order for you. Eight of those huge jars for growing herbs and things in. Customer bought two and back the next week to order eight more.'

'Grand,' said Mr Manders, writing down the order while Jinny wandered round the shop. It wasn't a tartan trash gift shop, but full of things that you didn't see anywhere else. Nell Storr bought nearly all her stock directly from the craftsmen who made it.

Jinny was looking longingly at some wood carvings when her father called her over.

'This is Jinny,' he said, and Nell held out her hand, purple nail-varnished and heavy with rings.

'Nell was saying that she might be interested in selling some of your drawings,' said Mr Manders. 'Pity we didn't think – you could have brought some of them with you.'

'Have you a sketchbook on you?' asked Nell. 'I know I never move without mine.'

Jinny knew that she still had her sketchpad in her pocket. She hesitated. Normally she would never have shown her drawings to anyone, but if Nell bought some, and paid her for them, Jinny would have money of her own: perhaps enough money to buy a saddle for Shantih, for when the ponies went back to their trekking they would be taking their tack with them.

Jinny studied Nell. She liked the bright kaftan she was wearing, the painted eyes, the fuzz of black hair and the face that was ugly but interesting. Jinny decided to risk it. She took the pad out of her pocket, laid it on the counter, and began slowly to turn over the pages.

The first drawings were of Shantih galloping, done in Indian ink with watercolour washes. Then there were some of Kelly, two or three of Mr MacKenzie and his sheep, one of Bramble's head, and a few of an enormous spider she had met in Bramble's stall. Then there were the drawings she had done that morning of the ospreys.

'So you've been to Loch Garten?' asked Nell.

'Oh, no,' said Jinny, 'I drew them on the moor this morning.'

'But surely that's an osprey?' Nell took the sketchpad from Jinny and turned it to her last drawing of the hawk taking a fish from the loch. 'Yes. There it is, an osprey.'

Jinny felt her face flood crimson. She looked helplessly at her father and at the tall, bald man who was standing next to him and had been looking at Jinny's drawings while he waited to be served.

' 'Fraid we've never made Loch Garten. Not on the money you pay me. Jinny copied them from Mike's bird book.'

Nell looked intently at the drawings and Jinny knew that she didn't believe her father.

'Mike's bird book or not,' said Nell. 'I like them. I'll give you a fiver for four of the horse sketches. I'll mount them on coloured card, mark them up at two pounds each and if they sell we can discuss terms.'

'Oh, thank you. Yes. Thank you very much indeed.'

Nell chose the four drawings she wanted and gave Jinny a five pound note.

'Excuse me,' said the man, who had been listening. 'I would like to purchase one of your drawings of the osprey. They are beautifully done. You have a great gift and it pleases me to see proof that the human hand is still superior to the machine – that the camera is still inferior to the work of an artist. You see not with, but through the eye.'

Jinny snatched her pad and stuffed it into her pocket.

'They're not for sale,' she stated. 'My brother wants them. He only lent me his book so that I'd draw them for him.'

'If that is so perhaps you could tell me your address, and later I will write to you to see if you have been making any more bird drawings.'

'You needn't bother,' said Jinny, 'because I shan't be. I only draw horses.'

The man had a face creased like the skin on sour milk, pebble glasses that magnified his eyes, and a morticed mouth.

'My apologies,' he said to Mr Manders. 'I did not mean to offend.'

An assistant came bustling up and the man walked away with her.

'Stranger to me,' said Nell. 'Liked your work though. Be sure to let me see some more of it the next time Tom's coming in.'

Back in the car Jinny looked despairingly at her father.

'I forgot they were in it,' she said.

'Can't be helped now. Didn't like the way that man was so interested in them.'

'Well, he doesn't know where I saw it. I didn't give him our address.'

'He saw me bringing in the pots. They're all marked Finmory. Or he's only to ask Nell. Still, spilt milk. Now let's go and see about buying you some respectable clothes.'

Buying the anorak was quite painless. The first one Jinny tried on fitted her. Walking back through the store they passed a rail with a notice above it saying *'Sale Garments. Uncollected orders made to measure.'* Jinny looked at them as she walked past. There were skirts and trousers and at the end of the rail a pair of jodhpurs. Jinny grabbed her father's hand.

'Look,' she cried, and lifted the jodhpurs off the rail. She held them against herself. 'They'd fit me,' she said.

'Eight pounds fifty,' said the assistant. 'Very best quality reduced from twenty pounds. We've had rather a lot of trouble trying to sell them. In fact, to tell you the truth, they've been with us for a year now. Too long a leg fitting for the average size.'

'If they fit, you pay three and I'll pay the rest,' said Mr Manders.

Jinny took them into a fitting room and wriggled into them. They were a bit wide at the waist, but apart from that they fitted perfectly.

'Just think,' said Jinny to her father as they drove home, 'all the time we've been at Finmory these jodhs have been waiting for me.'

'A beautiful thought,' agreed her father.

'D'you know,' Jinny confided, 'I think my life is caught in a whirlpool. Everything is happening to me. Everything! And tomorrow I'm taking Shantih to Craigvaar, and I'm learning to jump, and I've sold some of my drawings, and now if I got to the Inverburgh Show I've got jodhpurs to wear!'

'Oh, Jinny,' said her father, 'slow down.'

But Jinny didn't hear him. She was riding Shantih over the jumps in Clare's paddock, soaring clear and high over them all while Clare watched in admiration.

Eight

Clare drove the horsebox up the drive to Finmory. The low branches of the trees rattled against its sides and it swayed from side-to-side as the wheels caught in ruts.

'Jinny,' called her mother, 'Clare's here.'

Frantically Jinny stared at her reflection in her wardrobe mirror. She could not make up her mind whether to wear her new jodhpurs or not. She had put them on and taken them off three times already. They certainly looked smart, but somehow Jinny felt they were too dressed-up to wear when she was only going to Craigvaar.

She heard the horsebox stopping and struggled out of the jodhpurs.

'I'll keep them new,' she decided, 'in case I do go to Inverburgh Show with Clare,' and with relief Jinny pulled on her usual jeans. She ran downstairs and out to the stables where Shantih was waiting, groomed and shining, already suspicious that something unusual was going to happen to her.

'You can take the box round to the back,' Mr Manders told Clare. 'Think Jinny's round there.'

Slowly the box trundled round the side of the house and across to the stable.

'Nag ready?' Clare asked, jumping down from the cab.

'She is,' said Jinny, 'but Mummy wanted to know if you'd like a cup of tea?'

'Oh dear,' said Clare. 'Do you think she'd be frightfully upset if I didn't? Would it be rather rude? It's just that I would like to give my beasts a really decent exercise today. Poor dears didn't get out at all yesterday, and I thought if you came over now we could have lunch at home and then get them out for a good long ride. Got to keep them on the ball for the show. I don't know what Pa would say if Huston didn't win.'

'It doesn't matter,' said Jinny. 'It was only if you wanted one.'

Mr Manders came up and Jinny introduced him to Clare.

'Jinny was telling me that you're a potter. Now I do think that's terribly clever. I'm just hopeless at anything like that.'

'Only moderate myself,' admitted Mr Manders. 'It's Ken that's the potter.'

'Ken?'

'He's a friend who stays with us,' explained Mr Manders, and Jinny asked quickly if she should bring Shantih out. She didn't particularly want Ken to meet Clare.

'I'll get the ramp down,' said Clare. 'Has she been boxed before?'

'Yes,' said Jinny, suddenly remembering that the last horsebox that Shantih had been in had crashed. If she had remembered before she would have thought of some way of stopping Clare bringing her horsebox to Finmory. Jinny was suddenly certain that Shantih would remember the accident.

She put Shantih's halter on, knotting it securely at the noseband, and started to lead her out of the stable. Shantih stopped dead in the doorway, her front legs braced, eyes goggling, ears almost meeting with surprise at the sight of the horsebox.

'It's all right,' Jinny assured her. 'It won't hurt you. Come and look at it. There's a good horse. Come on now.'

'Bit spooky is she?' demanded Clare.

'The last horsebox she was in was hit by a lorry,' Jinny explained. 'I expect she remembers it,' and she scratched Shantih's neck and rubbed her shoulder, whispering encouragement to her as she took a hesitant step forward.

'There's the horse,' said Jinny. 'That's the way.' And

Shantih allowed herself to be persuaded to walk out of the stable doorway.

Jinny managed to lead her towards the box and to turn her to face the ramp but then Shantih froze and refused to move another step.

'Get her going,' said Clare.

'Why have you stopped?' said Mr Manders. 'Go on, take her into the box.'

'What do you think I'm trying to do?' asked Jinny, scowling at them both.

'Wake her up then,' shouted Clare. 'Haven't you got a stick? Here – I'll chase her for you,' and Clare came striding towards Shantih, waving her arms and shouting.

Shantih snorted through wide nostrils and plunged away from her, almost knocking Jinny down.

'Don't,' warned Jinny. 'If you upset her she'll never go near the box.'

'I'll upset her,' threatened Clare. 'She's needing someone who can straighten her out. I haven't got all day to stand around here you know.'

'Just give her a minute,' said Jinny, hanging on desperately to the halter rope while Shantih tugged back, half rearing, tossing her head from side to side. Jinny was afraid that it was too late already. Now that Shantih was fighting them they would never manage to force her into the box. They should have coaxed her in with oats or led Punch in and out to let her see that it was safe.

'Don't be silly,' pleaded Jinny. 'It's only a horse-box. Nothing will happen to you. Come on, Shantih, come on.'

In Jinny's own ears her voice sounded anxious and impatient. If Jinny had heard that voice speaking in a foreign language she wouldn't have trusted it either.

'Oh, don't be daft. It's quite safe, Shantih. You're all right. Come on now.'

The mare was electric with panic. The gaping black entrance to the horsebox was filled with lurking terrors. She plunged and fought at the end of the halter. Jinny hung on, conscious of Clare's heavy-browed irritation, her father's recording presence and her own feebleness. But most of all she was thinking how beautiful Shantih was when she was like this, all bright burning energy, defying them all.

'I'm not standing here watching a horse muck around like that,' announced Clare. 'Don't think your daughter is fit to cope with her,' she said to Mr Manders. 'Here, give me the rope. I'll get her into the box.'

Reluctantly, Jinny relinquished the halter. 'She won't go in now,' she said.

'We'll see about that,' said Clare. She yanked at the halter rope, pulling at Shantih's head, shouting at her, grim threats that were hardly more than a roar in Clare's throat. 'Get up with you, you brute, garn you, you twister you.'

Jinny fiddled with a strand of her hair. A hard lump

choked in her throat. She hadn't wanted it to be like this. If it had been anyone else treating Shantih as roughly as Clare was doing Jinny would have been snatching her horse back, but somehow it was different with Clare. Jinny had to believe in Clare, that she knew what was best. She so longed to be part of Clare's life, to know someone who was strong and confident like Clare seemed to be, who rode at shows and hunted and knew all about horses. To believe in Clare made these things possible for Jinny as well.

'Watch yourself with her,' warned Mr Manders. 'She's not used to being bossed around.'

'That's her trouble,' answered Clare. 'Go into the front of the box,' she shouted to Jinny. 'I think there's a stick in there.'

'It's no use . . .' Jinny began.

'You're not going to let her get away with this, are you?' Clare's dull eyes challenged Jinny. She stood playing Shantih like a salmon on the end of a line, her heavy bulk holding her to the ground while Shantih flashed and fought not to go any closer to the box.

'Go on, get it,' ordered Clare.

Jinny climbed into the cabin of the box and lying on top of the dashboard was a long cutting whip. Reluctantly Jinny picked it up. Inside the cabin, Clare's shouting and the trampling of Shantih's hooves were muted. Jinny sat for a second staring through the windscreen, holding the stick. She didn't want to take it out to Clare. She knew that hitting Shantih was useless.

'Can't you find it?' demanded Clare.

Jinny jumped down from the cab and walked slowly back to Clare.

'I never hit her. It only makes her fight more.'

'We'll see about that,' said Clare, grabbing the stick. 'Now, my lady, let's see who's boss,' and Clare swung the stick at Shantih's shoulder. But before it could touch her Shantih had reared straight up as she had been trained to do in the circus. Her forehooves lashed out at Clare's head. Jinny heard Clare scream, saw the sunlight dazzle on Shantih's metal shoes before she flung herself forward and threw her arms round Shantih's neck. Mr Manders, too, dashed forward and grabbed the rope from Clare.

Shantih's forelegs touched the ground. She tried to rear again but Jinny's weight on her neck and Mr Manders' hold on the rope stopped her from going up again. She pulled back violently, flinging herself away from them, then she stood trembling.

'Did she get you?' Mr Manders asked Clare.

'Well, what a temper!' exclaimed Clare. 'No, she missed me, filthy brute that she is.'

'She's not, she's not,' protested Jinny. 'She doesn't mean to behave like that,' and Jinny took Shantih from her father and led her away from the horsebox. 'We've made her so afraid, she doesn't know what she's doing.'

'You're not going to give in to her?' said Clare. 'If she were mine she'd go into the box or else.'

'She's afraid,' said Jinny again. 'Lots of people are afraid to get into a car again after they've had an accident even when they know that it's not likely to happen to them again, but you can't tell a horse. They can't understand that the same thing isn't bound to happen.'

'Well, what are you going to do? I can't waste any more time. I mean to say one can't stand around being made a fool of by a horse.'

'I'll ride her over to Craigvaar this afternoon,' suggested Jinny.

'Well, just as you like,' said Clare. 'I must say I'm not used to giving in to animals, but if that's your idea of how to treat a horse it's up to you, of course.'

'It might be the safest thing,' said Mr Manders.

'One might say the safest thing would be to get rid of the brute before she does some real damage,' said Clare scornfully. 'But of course it is entirely up to yourselves. I'll see you later, if she doesn't decide that she wants to stay in her field.'

Clare jarred the horsebox into motion, swung it round and roared past the house, down the drive and out onto the road.

'What a carry on!' exclaimed Mr Manders.

Jinny stared down at Shantih, who was grazing nervously. The whole atmosphere was stirred and shaken by the sudden violence. Jinny could almost feel the disturbance lapping to and fro like shattered ripples on a pond.

'Does Shantih go for you like that?' Mr Manders asked.

'It's only when you have a stick. She's just terrified,' said Jinny, stroking Shantih's damp neck and running her fingers through her mane.

'If I didn't find Clare Burnley so offensive I might almost believe that she's right. Shantih does seem to go mad. You know, she is dangerous, Jinny. Mr MacKenzie was telling us how she keeps throwing you off when you're trying to ride her.'

'That's why I'm taking her to Clare's, isn't it?' said Jinny crossly. 'Clare is going to help me school her.'

'She wasn't very successful this morning,' said Mr Manders. 'Do you really want to take her to Craigvaar? Isn't there anyone else who could help you? How about Miss Tuke?'

'She's too busy trekking,' said Jinny. 'And anyway I want to go. Clare's won rosettes and cups and everything. She knows about horses. Miss Tuke only knows about trekking ponies.'

'Well, for goodness' sake be careful.'

'I will,' said Jinny. 'I will. I'm never anything else.'

After lunch Jinny caught Shantih and rode to Craigvaar. At least, she rode as far as the farm. Shantih wasn't keen to pass Mr MacKenzie's tractor, which was throbbing in the yard and, since Mr MacKenzie was standing in the yard too, Jinny thought she had better dismount and lead Shantih past the tractor before she was bucked off.

She coaxed Shantih past the tractor, waved to Mr MacKenzie, and walked on out of sight of the farm. She was just about to remount when she changed her mind. It was far too nice a day to go on fighting. Jinny ran up her stirrups and slackened the girth.

'Let's have a happy time,' she said to Shantih. 'Let's stop all this aggro.'

Shantih snuffled at Jinny's neck, denying that she ever fought with anyone. Jinny laughed as the horse's long whiskers tickled her.

'It is you just as much as me,' Jinny told her, but she knew this wasn't true. Shantih hadn't fought when Ken was riding her.

Walking at Shantih's head, Jinny felt suddenly happy. Wherever she looked there were signs of spring. New life stretching up to the sun, flowers and leaves uncurling, lambs with the sheep, rabbits that were too young to know any better nibbling at the side of the road until Shantih and Jinny were almost upon them. The sun was warm again, and Jinny could feel it burning the back of her neck.

'It's spring,' Jinny told Shantih, skipping at her side. 'The winter's had it. Wonder if I could take you for a swim in the sea?'

With Shantih walking companionably by her side, Jinny felt perfectly content. There was nothing more she could have asked for. The wild country stretching around her, the grace of Shantih and the sun's warmth were all Jinny needed. All she would ever need.

Jinny paused before she turned the bend of the track that would bring Craigvaar into view. She took a last long look over the moorland to the mountains that were close today and seemed to be almost moving as the light flowed in mauves and greys and brilliance over their hunched shoulders. In the opposite direction the sea glimmered and sparkled and dark specks of gulls soared above it, weaving land to sea, sea to sky.

Why isn't it enough? Jinny thought wretchedly. *Enough to live here and have Shantih with me? Why can't this feeling last?*

She didn't know why, only knew that she had to go on going on. She tightened her girths and climbed back onto Shantih.

When they reached Craigvaar, fearing that Shantih might get a fright and bolt over the perfect lawns, Jinny dismounted again and led her up the path. She rang the front doorbell and waited.

'Darling,' said Mrs Burnley, opening the door. 'Clare waited ages for you but she thought you weren't coming. She's taken both the boys out by herself, poor thing. They can be quite a handful for one person to cope with. Now she said if you turned up you're to

129

put your fellow in one of the spare boxes and wait until she gets back.'

Self-consciously, Jinny led Shantih down through the long garden, between the rhododendrons and on to the stable yard. The doors of Huston's and Jasper's boxes were open wide. Jinny put Shantih into one of the other boxes. She hesitated, wondering whether she should take Shantih's tack off. It seemed silly to leave it on but pushy to take it off. Jinny decided to leave it on until Clare came back. She filled a bucket and gave Shantih a drink, then leaned against the half door chatting to her, the Arab's breath sweet on her face, the sun warm.

'If only we lived here,' Jinny said longingly. 'Imagine if these boxes and all the tack belonged to us. I'll bet you I wouldn't come off so much if I'd a proper saddle with knee rolls instead of those old trekking saddles.'

It was nearly an hour before Clare came back. Jinny heard the distant clatter of hooves on the road, then the sound of Clare's voice shouting at her horses. She came down over the moor and into the yard through the paddock gate. She was riding Huston and leading Jasper, who dragged behind at the full length of his reins.

'So you've persuaded her to come. Glad to see she's not a completely free agent. Thought you might have been over sooner. These two are pigs to take out by oneself. I'm utterly destroyed. And with a valuable beast like Jasper I mean to say one is absolutely on tenterhooks in case he even scratches himself.'

Clare dismounted and handed Huston's reins to Jinny.

'We'll settle them for the night,' she said. 'I know it is far too early but we're out for dinner with the Cranshaws and goodness knows when we'll arrive back. Do you know them? Old Pinkie Cranshaw is an absolute old sweetie. Flatters outrageously but you know how one does enjoy it.'

Jinny didn't.

'Shall I take Huston's tack off?' she asked.

'Tack off, water, quick groom, rug on, bed down and I'll bring their hay and feed.'

'I've put Shantih in the box next to Huston,' said Jinny, really wanting to ask if she should give Shantih some hay too.

'See to her after Huston,' said Clare. 'I like to get these two attended to whenever they come in from exercise. Of course, Barbara sees to all this sort of thing when we're at home, but one does feel terribly responsible when she's not here to cope.'

Before she started to groom Huston, Jinny took Shantih's tack off. If Clare was going out for dinner it didn't look as if she would have time to school Shantih. Jinny didn't know whether she was disappointed or relieved.

When all three horses were munching their feeds, Clare and Jinny went up to the house for afternoon tea. They had it in the sun lounge with Mrs Burnley pouring and telling Jinny how she loved her perfectly sweet hair.

'Would it be terribly rude of me not to run you back to Finmory? Daddy is just too fussy about punctuality and I absolutely must have a bath before I go out. I mean one couldn't bear to have Pinkie telling one how absolutely divine one looks when all the time one is ponging of horse.'

Jinny said she could easily walk.

'I'll come over for you first thing tomorrow morning and we'll give my two a thorough good exercise before I try to lunge your brute.'

'I won't be able to come until about twelve,' Jinny said. It was her day to take the early watch at the ospreys' nest. Ken had taken her turn today and she didn't think she could ask him again.

'Oh lordy no! But what a bore. Why ever not? Twelve o'clock! That's half the day gone. Why can't you come earlier? I mean to say I thought that was why you were here, so we could ride together.'

'I've jobs to do at home,' Jinny said.

'But how quaint. Of course Heather and Pat do all that sort of thing for us. Well, if you won't I suppose you won't. One can only hope that the afternoon is fine. It seems a frightful waste to me.'

Jinny said goodnight to Shantih, who was tugging at her hay net and hardly bothered to look round, then she walked home over the moors. She felt cold and empty and didn't know why. Hadn't she got what she wanted? Clare to help her school Shantih. Wasn't that what she'd wanted since she'd first heard about Clare?

As she walked, Jinny searched the sky for any sign of the ospreys, but there were only the usual crows and gulls and once the arrowed flight of a kestrel. It would be another four weeks before Peter and Brian expected the eggs to hatch. Once the young birds were out of their eggs there would be no more danger from egg collectors. Jinny grinned to herself, thinking about watching the young ospreys growing and learning to fly.

Birds out of eggs, she thought, wrinkling up her nose in amazement at the thought of an egg very much the same as the boiled one she had had for breakfast growing into an osprey.

As Jinny made her way towards Finmory she looked down at the road. There was a man walking towards Glenbost. Jinny couldn't think who he might be. In Stopton nearly everyone had been strangers but in Glenbost nobody was.

The man was tall with a bald head. He was looking round as he walked and Jinny saw the sun sparkling on his glasses. She didn't know who he could be and yet there was something familiar about him.

Need to ask Mr MacKenzie, she thought, but long before she reached home, she had forgotten all about him.

'We're going to lunge Shantih tomorrow,' Jinny told her mother.

'In American racing stables they have a machine which they hook the horses on to and they have to go round and round until you unhook them,' said Ken, talking to Kelly.

'Fancy that now,' said Jinny, and she took her handful of biscuits up to her bedroom and ate them looking down over the garden to the sea.

The field looked strangely empty with only Punch and Bramble in it.

I won't leave her at Craigvaar too long, Jinny thought. *Once Clare has shown me what I'm doing wrong I'll bring her home again.* But the cold emptiness was still there, like knowing you had an appointment with the dentist.

I'm daft, thought Jinny. *I really am daft. When I get what I wanted I don't want it any more.*

She found her book on schooling and read the chapter on lungeing over again, and as she read she saw herself in Clare's paddock, Shantih cantering smoothly on the lunge rein, relaxed and willing, because Clare had all the right things – a cavesson noseband and a proper lungeing rein. Clare knew the right way to school horses.

Yet there was still an emptiness in Jinny, a strange coldness.

Nine

It was after twelve the next morning before Jinny rode Bramble into the stable yard at Craigvaar. Shantih and Huston were looking out over their half doors. Shantih whinnied to Bramble and Jinny, wrinkling the velvet of her nose, pushing against the door to reach them. Beside Huston's huge, blank, Roman-nosed head, Shantih's delicate, dished face and wide, dark eyes looked more magical than ever. Jinny shivered with delight at her beauty, and was caught suddenly by the throat, feeling ridiculous tears springing into her eyes as she thought that Shantih was her horse. She slid down from Bramble and rubbed Shantih's neck, holding out her hand to feel Shantih lipping at it.

Clare came out of Jasper's box, a body brush in her hand.

'I'm sorry I'm so late,' Jinny said. 'I couldn't get

away any sooner. Mummy kept finding things for me to do.'

Really it had been Mike's fault. He should have relieved Jinny at eleven but he hadn't arrived at the hide until half past.

'And I told you to be early today,' Jinny had said, snatching Bramble's reins. 'You know I asked you to be early because I've to be at Clare's. You wait, you just wait until you want me to draw something for you.'

'Make no difference,' said Mike. 'Miss Broughton always knows when you've drawn my things. Any egg collectors?'

'Thousands,' said Jinny.

All the time she had been at the hide the male osprey had sat, hardly blinking an eye, perched on the top branch of his favourite pine, while the hen was almost hidden in the nest as she brooded the eggs. Longing to be at Craigvaar, Jinny had been tempted to leave them.

There's not a chance of anyone finding them, not a chance, she thought, as she swept the hillside with the powerful glasses. Sheep nibbled undisturbed, hoodie crows flapped lazily from rock to rock and a ginger cat from the farm sat petrified, waiting for rabbits. *Mike's bound to be here soon. Why shouldn't I go?*

But she couldn't bring herself to leave the hide. The thought of what the others would say if anything happened to the eggs while she should have been on guard was enough to keep her there.

'I've mucked out your mare,' Clare said. 'Couldn't leave her standing there. Can't do that sort of thing when one's not used to it.'

'I am sorry,' said Jinny again.

''Course, when one's had horses all one's life one rather takes it for granted. If one has a horse one jolly well looks after it and that's all there is to it.'

'I won't be late again,' promised Jinny, wondering how she was ever going to fit in taking her turn at the hide with being at Craigvaar. 'It was just this morning.'

'Far too late to exercise them now. Better have lunch first and then get them out for a really good turn this afternoon.'

Jinny agreed.

'I'll give Jasper a go on the lunge. Shove that fellow in a box and you can come and watch. Pick up a few hints for your idiot.'

Jinny quickly put Bramble into the last empty box. She felt that she was making a take-over bid for Clare's stables.

'He won't need any hay,' she apologised to Clare. 'He's fat enough.' But Clare didn't seem to hear her. She had the lunge rein clipped to the cavesson and, with the driving whip in her hand, was leading Jasper down to the paddock. Jinny scuttled to open the gate for her.

'Lead him round a few times,' Clare said, as she took Jasper into the centre of the paddock.

Jinny grasped the supple leather of the headcollar and led the thoroughbred in a wide circle. He was remote and cold, a metallic horse, whose mind was made up of cogs and wheels.

When Jinny let him go, Clare sent him on at a trot. Jinny stood well back and watched as the black horse flung himself forward into a gallop. She saw Clare brace herself against him. She moved in a small circle, gradually bringing the horse back from his wild outburst of speed to a collected canter, controlling him between lunge rein and whip.

Jinny watched intently. It was the first time she had seen a horse being lunged. Clare was doing no more than Jinny's book had told her to do, but actually seeing Clare made all the difference. As if her skill was infectious.

'What about your blood?' Clare asked, when she had finished lungeing Jasper. 'D'you want me to have a go at her?'

Jinny hesitated.

'Well, if that's the way you feel! I rather got the message than you were wanting a bit of help, and let's face it, after yesterday's performance one might say you bloomin' well need some.'

'Oh, I do want you to help me,' cried Jinny. 'Of course I do. It's just that she's so terrified of whips there's no point in trying to lunge her with a whip in your hand. She'll only go crazy when she sees it. I know she will.'

'Actually,' stated Clare, 'I don't much fancy coping with her unless I have something in my hand. She wasn't kidding yesterday. She meant it. When she reared up she meant to get me.'

'It isn't her fault,' pleaded Jinny. 'It was that filthy circus. They taught her to do that. It was her act.'

'Tell you what, you put on her tack and I'll ride her round. I'll not use a stick but I rather think she'll find me harder to shift than she does you.'

'Be good,' Jinny whispered to Shantih as she put on her saddle and bridle. 'Do what Clare asks. You've got to learn to behave yourself. If you don't, they'll stop me from riding you, I know they will.'

High-stepping at Jinny's side, Shantih plunged down to the paddock. Her neck was crested, her tail, fanning out in the spring breeze, was kinked over her back. At the paddock gate she stuck her pint-pot head into the air, screaming through the dark pits of her nostrils.

She seemed to Jinny to be a golden horse out of legend, and for a second she admitted the truth of Ken's disgust with saddles and bridles. If Shantih were free she would rear up from the mountain tops, soar through the sky like a comet, racing to join the horses of the sun.

'I'll say this for Arabs, they are pretty little things,' said Clare, taking Shantih from Jinny, 'but I couldn't be bothered with one myself. Far too finicky. I've never known one that wasn't slightly potty.'

Clare mounted, lengthened her stirrups and sent Shantih forward at a walk. She rode with a deep, secure seat and a short rein, her hands fixed and unyielding. With Clare riding her, Shantih seemed to shrink in front of Jinny's eyes. When she plunged forward and began to buck Clare sat solid and unmoved, kicking her on and shouting at her.

After Shantih's fourth buck Clare won. She managed to get Shantih's head up and send her on round the paddock.

'Go on,' growled Clare. 'Get on, you twisted vampire. Get on with you,' and she pressed Shantih relentlessly into a gallop. Round and round she galloped her, and even when Shantih would have slowed down to a trot Clare forced her to go on galloping.

Jinny watched numbly. This was what Shantih needed. Clare wasn't being cruel. She hadn't used a stick. This was why Jinny had brought her horse to Craigvaar so that Clare would ride her. But was this really what she wanted? Jinny didn't know.

Clare brought Shantih back to a walk, turned her and took her round in the opposite direction. Shantih stopped. Clare roared at her and Shantih reared straight up. Clare slackened her reins, leaning forward, but she didn't move an inch in the saddle. She was as secure as if she were sitting on a rocking horse. Shantih's second rear was less defiant, and as she touched the ground again Clare was ready for her, and with seat and voice she forced her forward. In seconds, Shantih was tearing round the paddock at a flat out gallop.

Jinny tried not to look. She couldn't bear the sight of Clare galloping her horse; couldn't bear the sight of Shantih's straining body, foam-spattered chest and frantic, panic-blind eyes. Jinny clenched herself tight.

'It's what she needs, it's what she needs,' she told herself, but really what she wanted to do was to grab Clare and drag her to the ground and never let her go near Shantih again.

'That's straightened her out a bit for you,' Clare announced at last as she walked Shantih back to Jinny. 'We'll get her head strapped down – stop her rearing. You're far too soft with her. That's half the trouble. One has to treat a horse as a horse or it ends up being the boss.'

Jinny knew she should say something, should thank Clare and praise her riding, but she couldn't bring herself to do it.

'Don't think there's time for you to have a shot,' said Clare. 'We want to get lunch over and get out. Anyway, she's had enough for today. Let the lesson sink in.'

Jinny led Shantih back to her box. She didn't think Clare had taught her anything, only been rough with her and proved that she was a stronger rider than Jinny. She took Shantih's tack off and rubbed her down with a straw wisp. Shantih's sides were clamped in and she stood in a corner of the box with her ears gloomed back and her tail tucked down. Clare came to the door to say that lunch was ready and Jinny followed her out, too ashamed to look back at Shantih.

In the afternoon they exercised Clare's horses. Clare, on Jasper, rode at Jinny's side, telling her stories of her horsey past.

'But really I do think my favourite was Ladybird. She was fantastic at games. The other kids just would not enter when they saw us lining up. I honestly swear that she could have won a bending race by herself.'

Listening to Clare, Jinny forgot about the morning, forgot about the way Clare had ridden Shantih. She could only think how wonderful Clare was, how much Clare knew about horses and how amazing it was that she should be talking to her like this.

'My first real hunter was a big bay horse. I came home for the Christmas hols and there she was. Sixteen hands! Well, you can imagine what one felt. I'd been riding a fourteen-two pony in the summer. One felt really grown up at last. And my first hunt on her! Gosh, all the gates seemed tiny. Blitz just stepped over them. And one knew how madly jealous all one's friends were. I mean to say, most of them were still grubbing about on ponies.'

As they rode back to Craigvaar, Jinny saw a stranger walking down the road towards them. It was the same man she had seen yesterday, the same bald head and glasses. Jinny peered at him curiously. She still felt she should know him but couldn't place him. It wasn't until he was almost level with the horses that Jinny remembered. She caught her breath in surprise, turned quickly to Clare hiding from the man beneath her hard hat, for it was the customer from the Inverburgh gift shop and he had binoculars round his neck.

'Did you know that chap?' Clare asked. Jinny shook her head. 'Seemed to know you. Odd-looking type. Birdwatcher, I expect.'

Jinny told her father that she had seen the man again.

'So he's found out where we came from,' said Mr Manders. 'I'll warn the others. Of course, he may be perfectly innocent, only wanting to see the ospreys.'

Jinny wasn't so sure. She hadn't liked him.

'He was a grabber,' she said. 'Wanted to grab my drawings.'

Next morning Jinny was at Craigvaar early. She had mucked out the horses before Clare appeared.

'How kind,' said Clare. 'Now we'll be able to get these two out at a decent hour.'

'I have to be home for three o'clock,' said Jinny. She had to take the afternoon watch on the nest and felt it would be better to let Clare know straightaway.

'You do lead a busy little life,' said Clare. 'What is it this time, down the salt mines or to the galleys?'

When they had exercised Huston and Jasper, Clare suggested they should try lungeing Shantih.

'No whip,' said Jinny.

'You can ride her and I'll lunge you both,' said Clare, and gave Jinny a martingale and a drop noseband to try on Shantih.

'Put your stirrups down two holes,' ordered Clare, when she had Jinny and Shantih in the paddock. 'You're perched on top of her and when she starts playing up you've no control. That's better. Now walk her round.'

Jinny took Shantih round. With longer stirrups she was able to use her legs more strongly and push Shantih on when she tried to break out of the circle.

'Good,' yelled Clare. 'Now let's try her at a trot.'

Shantih burst forward into a canter, then tried to buck, but the lunge rein kept her head up.

'No you don't, you twister. Get on with you,' roared Clare.

Jinny, sitting deeper in the saddle than she normally did, was able to push Shantih on where before she would have been jerked out of the saddle and the horse would have been in control.

'Nicely. Well done,' shouted Clare. 'Now try and balance her. Push with your seat. Keep her there between your hands and your seat. Good. Not too fast. Slow trot. Good. Keep her there.'

Concentrating on obeying Clare's instructions, Jinny hardly realised that Shantih had trotted round several times without bucking.

'Walk,' shouted Clare. 'Change the rein.'

Jinny looked down doubtfully at her reins.

'It means walk across the circle and go round in the opposite direction.'

'Oh,' said Jinny, and did so.

'This time when I say, "prepare to trot, trot on," that's what I want – not a canter and then a bucking display.'

Jinny nodded, all her attention on her horse.

'Prepare to trot.'

Jinny shortened her reins and sat down in the saddle.

'Trot on.'

Jinny, letting Shantih go forward, felt the moment when normally Shantih would have been bucking, but now she was able to check her, bring her back and collect her between her hands and her seat. For the very first time Jinny felt as if she were in control of Shantih and not the other way round.

In half an hour Clare said Shantih had had enough.

'Thank you very much,' said Jinny. 'She was much better, wasn't she?'

'You've got a good seat,' said Clare. 'I expect it's all the bashing about you've done on those Highlands. Keep your stirrups at that length and perhaps you'll be able to stay on top of her for a change.'

'I think she understood what we wanted her to do,' said Jinny. 'I think she enjoyed it too.'

'Taking her to the show on Wednesday?' asked Clare, joking.

'Oh, I couldn't,' gasped Jinny, but visions of herself and Shantih trotting round a show ring lit up in neon lights behind her eyes. 'But I couldn't.'

'Why not? They have this thing called Handy Horse. Actually, it's only a showing class for horses who aren't good enough to show. You go round the ring all together, trot up and canter back, get on and off, and that's it. No jumping. Of course she may not win, but as long as you don't expect that, there's nothing to it. Room in the box for her.'

'She wouldn't go in,' said Jinny.

'I'll put Huston and Jasper in first. Might be a bit of a laugh taking an Arab to Inverburgh. Some of them won't know what she is. Nearly all cows and sheep.'

'You don't really think I could?'

Clare laughed scornfully. 'I'm not suggesting you take her to the White City,' she said. 'You're so intense about everything. She's only a horse. Have a bit of fun on her for a change.'

'Do you think I could?' repeated Jinny longingly.

'Well, I jolly well would in your shoes. That's what horses are for, to get you out and about a bit. Goodness, when I was your age I was absolutely mad on Pony Club things. I would have gone anywhere.'

When Jinny told her family that she was taking Shantih to Inverburgh Show, there was a moment of silent amazement.

'But . . .' began Mrs Manders.

'But you . . .' gasped Petra.

'You'll be thrown off in front of everyone,' cried Mike. 'If she gets the least little bit excited she bucks you off and she'll be out of her skin at a show.'

'Clare and I are schooling her,' said Jinny. 'Clare says I've got a good seat.'

'Good and hard,' said Mike, 'the number of times you've landed on it.'

'Isn't it too dangerous?' asked Mr Manders. 'She can't have improved so much in such a short time, and if she ran mad at the show she might hurt someone.'

'Actually, that's all a thing of the past,' said Jinny. 'Clare says that when she was my age she would have gone anywhere, that nothing would have stopped her. So it's not going to stop me.'

'Does this mean we'll need to count you out for the day of the show?' Peter asked. 'Wednesday, did you say? What watch are you doing?'

'It means,' said Jinny, taking a deep breath, 'that I won't be free until after the show.'

Jinny thought hard about riding Shantih in a show ring while everyone around her was shocked or annoyed or furious.

'I can't help it,' stated Jinny. 'I'll watch the ospreys as much as you like after Wednesday, but not before.'

'You can do Thursday then,' said Petra. 'It should be me from eleven to three and I want to go to Duniver that morning.'

'Anything after Wednesday,' said Jinny patiently. 'I don't suppose you have a hair net?' she asked her mother. 'Clare says I should wear a hair net,' and Mr Manders burst out laughing.

'If Clare told you to dance a hornpipe on top of Shantih you'd do it,' he said.

'Everyone with long hair wears a hair net when they're showing a horse,' Jinny told him.

Jinny spent Tuesday night at Craigvaar. Before they went to bed, she and Clare went out to say goodnight to the horses.

'So quaint,' said Clare. 'I just cannot believe that this will be the first horse show you've ever been to.'

'But it is,' said Jinny. 'My very first.'

She fed Shantih the bread crusts she had brought.

'Be good tomorrow,' Jinny said to her. 'I don't want you to win or anything like that. Just go into the box with Huston and Jasper and stay sensible when we're at the show.'

The whole of Jinny was twisted into a tight knot of excitement. Half of her was thrilled at the thought of riding Shantih in a show ring, while the other half of her was curled away from the thought; afraid that taking Shantih to a show was the stupidest thing she had ever done. Jinny knew that Shantih had improved. In the paddock that afternoon she had stayed calm and responsive, only trying to rear once; but what would she do at the show?

This time tomorrow it will all be over, Jinny thought, *and really, the worst thing that could happen is for me to come off, and I'm quite used to that.*

Ten

Jinny sat in the cabin of the horsebox, squashed between Mr Burnley, who was driving, and Clare. In the box behind them were the three horses. Shantih, tucked in behind Huston, had walked into the box with hardly any hesitation, which seemed to Jinny to be such a good omen that she felt anything was possible. Shantih might even win her class when the day had started so well.

'Same place as usual?' Mr Burnley demanded.

'Gosh yes,' said Clare. 'Shouldn't think they'd ever change it.'

Clare was wearing a black jacket, white breeches and boots. She had lent Jinny an old tweed hacking jacket, but even with this and her new jodhpurs Jinny still felt a thing of rags and patches beside Clare.

'But, darling, you look really sweet. Such wonderfully

151

pretty hair,' Mrs Burnley had said before they left, which let Jinny know that she didn't think much of her appearance either.

As if it matters, thought Jinny. *I don't care what I look like. The only thing that matters is for Shantih to go well.*

Mr Burnley turned the box through the gateway and onto the show field.

'We've come here some years and it's been hock deep in mud. Remember that spring when Spencer was on a little grey mare? Knew she wouldn't stand a chance in the heavy going, so he borrowed a carthorse thing from one of the farmers. Feet like sewer lids. And, by Jove, he won the jumping on it. Only animal who could stay upright. Old Spencer went round the lot. Remember that, Clare?'

Jinny stared through the cabin window as the box trundled over the field. White tents dazzled in the sun, stalls and caravans were surrounded by displays of goods for sale, and around the main ring a row of cars was already in place. There were pens of sheep and cattle as immaculate as advertisements in a butcher's shop window, and carthorses with their coats spiky with soap and their manes and stumpy tails bedecked with ribbons. Next to the carthorses were the Highland ponies and Shetlands, with long, dense manes and their tails sweeping the ground. Jinny shivered with excitement.

Mr Burnley parked the box in a far corner of the field.

'This is where all the horsey things go on,' Clare explained. 'I must admit we do rather take second place to the sheep, but it is such a friendly little show. Such fun!'

Through the window at the back of the cabin Jinny could see the three horses. They were all tied up short to the sides of the box, their eyes glinting in the dim light.

'All content?' Clare asked.

'Seem to be,' said Jinny.

'We'll dash across to the secretary's tent and collect our numbers before we take them out. My showing class will be first. Want to give Jasper a bit of a school before then.'

Clare jumped down from the cabin and Jinny followed her.

'Over this way,' said Clare, 'unless they've changed things, which one does not even consider.'

With long, springing strides Clare marched to the secretary's tent. Jinny, trotting beside her, thought that she seemed to know everyone. Permed, white-haired ladies in headscarves and sheepskins, farmers in bristling tweed suits, red-faced moustached men in bow ties and bowlers, and thin young men in sports jackets and twills all shouted greetings to Clare as she passed.

'Wonderful to see you,' Clare cried to them all. 'How one does absolutely love meeting everyone again.'

'Clare Burnley – numbers twelve and thirty-four,' said the lady at the table in the secretary's tent. 'So pleased to see you here again.'

'Absolutely wonderful to be here,' said Clare.

'No Spencer this year?'

''Fraid not. Staying with friends. Chance to get out with a gun that he couldn't bear to pass up.'

'Only seems like yesterday when he was in here entering for all the games,' lamented the lady.

'Jinny wants to enter for the Handy Horse comp,' organised Clare.

'Thirty pence entry fee.'

The lady gave Jinny number fifty-seven.

'I'll keep it for ever,' Jinny said as they walked back to the box.

'I should jolly well tie it on your arm just now,' said Clare, 'or you're bound to lose it and then there's such a fuss. I say, look, isn't that Ros? Oh, I must go and have a word with her,' and Clare ran across to a girl in a scarlet trouser suit and a white fur hat.

Gradually the whole show ground was filling up. Sheep were already being judged, farmers were putting a last-minute polish on their beasts, stall owners were shouting their wares, a clutch of gas-filled balloons sailed high above the tents, children rode round on shaggy ponies and a few adults exercised their horses.

The air was filled with noise and excitement. Standing waiting for Clare, Jinny shivered suddenly. She wished Clare would hurry up so that they could take Shantih out of the box and give her time to get used to the strange surroundings before it was her class.

Oh please, thought Jinny, *please let her behave herself*. Surrounded by all the noise and bustle, Jinny was beginning to realise that riding Shantih here wouldn't be the same as riding her in Clare's paddock.

'Terribly sorry,' said Clare, coming back at last. 'Have I been ages? Ros is such a sweet girl, so amusing, and I hadn't seen her for months.'

'Been a deuce of a time,' growled Mr Burnley. 'That's the first showing class in the ring just now.'

'Don't panic, darling,' said Clare, patting her father's arm. 'We've about two hours before it's us.'

In the small ring were eight or nine children's ponies.

'Gosh, I know them all so well,' exclaimed Clare. 'Every year the same old ponies with different kids bumping round on top.'

Mr Burnley lowered the ramp and Shantih screamed at them, rolling the whites of her eyes, tossing her head against the rope.

'Calm down,' shouted Clare. 'There's no need to look as if you were entering for the Derby. Lord, I hope she hasn't upset Jasper. Last thing I want is him breaking out – here,' she said to Jinny as she untied Shantih. 'Watch out for her.'

Jinny took Shantih's rope, uncertain just exactly what she was meant to be looking out for.

Feeling herself free, Shantih plunged out of the box in one enormous bound. The rope burnt through Jinny's hands and then Shantih was tearing at a flat-out gallop across the show field, the rope dangling about her legs.

'You bloomin' idiot,' swore Clare, but already Jinny was running after her horse, following in the wake of her disturbance.

Shantih had gone straight towards the line of Highland ponies. Jinny could hear them squealing and their owners shouting as she ran towards them. By the time Jinny reached them, a man in blue dungarees had caught Shantih and she was standing tense and afraid.

'This your property?'

'Oh, thank you for catching her,' cried Jinny. 'Are the ponies all right?'

'Wouldn't hang around to find out,' said the man, 'or they'll be sueing you for damages.'

Jinny took Shantih's rope and the Arab reared, shaking and tossing her head as she tried to escape again.

'You fit for her?' asked the man.

'She's excited,' said Jinny. 'Whoa, Shantih, whoa, steady. She doesn't know what she's doing when she gets a fright like this.'

'Hang on to her then,' said the man, keeping out of the reach of Shantih's hooves.

'Thank goodness you've got her,' said Clare, running up. 'Loose horse in a place like this can cause no end of damage. You were half asleep. I bloomin' warned you to look out. Honestly, Jinny, you'll need to start and look alive. I am not here to be a nursemaid to you. I expect that's her started. Don't tell me we are in for a day of her nonsense because I am just not going to stand for it!'

'I'm sorry,' said Jinny. It was taking all her strength to control Shantih. She seemed to be twice her usual size. Mighty as a war horse crying *ha* at the sound of trumpets, Shantih plunged and fought at the end of her rope.

'Give her to me,' ordered Clare. 'Now get up with you. No more of this nonsense.' Shantih flung up her head, wild and terrified. 'Get on with you, you twisted varmint.'

Back at the box, Clare put Shantih's bridle on. She gave the reins to Jinny.

'Now this time hold on to them. Take her across to that corner and let her graze for a bit. See if that will calm her down. She is a crazy squib.'

Shantih snatched up mouthfuls of grass between urgent screams to the other horses. Jinny refused to let herself think that she had been a fool to bring Shantih. She had done it and that was that. Now she had to see it through. But the sight of her horse, terrified and wild, stopped Jinny being blinded by the show's glamour. Perhaps Ken was right, and it was only pride that made people bring their animals to compete against each other.

'Your class is after mine,' Clare said, as she rode up mounted on Jasper. 'That is if you're still taking her in for it. I shouldn't blame you if you chicken out.'

'I'm not going home without trying,' said Jinny, and to her relief her voice sounded firm and confident, not quivering and jellified the way she was feeling.

'Pa will help you tack her up,' said Clare. 'I've got to school this fellow,' and she trotted away, sitting tall and solid on the showy black thoroughbred.

There was no sign of Mr Burnley at the horsebox, and Jinny had to struggle by herself to try and get the saddle on Shantih. She cavorted in circles, pulling Jinny round with her, and every time she got any length of rein she tried to plunge up the ramp to rejoin Huston.

'Can I give you a bit of help?' asked a boy from school.

'If you could hold her until I get her tack on,' Jinny said gratefully. 'It's this fiddling martingale.'

'She's a bonnie wee pony,' said Archie, clinging on to Shantih's bit.

Although it wasn't exactly how Jinny saw Shantih, it was the nicest thing anyone had said about her that morning.

'She gets a bit excited at times,' Jinny said, putting on her hard hat and trying to climb onto Shantih's back.

'My, but you're stiff,' said Archie. 'Is it the rheumatics you have?'

Jinny couldn't get her foot up to the stirrup. She hopped helplessly round, then realised that it was because of her new jodhpurs.

'Spring, girl, spring,' roared Mr Burnley. 'Never thought a skinned rabbit like you would be as stiff as that. Here, I'll chuck you up.'

'It's my new . . .' Jinny began, but before she could finish her explanation Mr Burnley had grasped her knee and thrown her skywards. Luckily Shantih shied away from him so when Jinny came down she landed on top of the saddle.

When she was mounted she felt better. She rode with long stirrups the way Clare had taught her, and sat deep in the saddle. At first, Shantih refused to pay any attention to her, but went on spooking and shying, barging her quarters into people, ponies and cars.

'It's all right,' Jinny told her. 'It's all right. Nothing's going to happen to you. I'm only going to ride you in the ring with a few other horses. Ride you up and down, that's all. We'll go back to Finmory soon, back to your own field. It's all right. Steady now. Don't get so excited, silly girl.'

As Jinny walked her round, threading their way through all the life of the show, she kept her voice low and gentle, whispering to Shantih the way Ken had done when he had ridden her over the moor, and gradually she felt the mare relaxing.

When Jinny came back to the ringside, Clare and eight other horses were riding round the ring. It was obvious that Jasper would be the winner. All the other horses were only ordinary riding horses, but Jasper was a top-class show horse.

That's not fair, Jinny thought. *He's much too good to be shown against those others. They don't stand a chance. Clare couldn't have known what they were going to be like or she wouldn't have entered him.*

Embarrassed, Jinny walked Shantih away and didn't take her back until the sound of applause told her that the class was over.

'Jolly good,' boomed Mr Burnley, as Clare rode out of the ring, a red rosette flapping from Jasper's bridle.

'Walkover,' Clare yelled back. 'Don't know why we bother to bring the cup back every year. Really, we could just keep it at home, and that would be that.'

Jinny tried not to listen. She concentrated on Shantih until the Handy Horse class was announced and she could ride away from the Burnleys and the circle of friends who were congratulating Clare.

Shantih pranced round the ring like a hackney; her hooves flashed neat and precise, her face was carven and delicate-featured, and her mane lifted in a silken wave.

There were six other horses and three Highland

ponies. Jinny saw Miss Tuke standing at the rails and waved, thinking that the Highlands were probably her trekkers. The six horses were duller, heavier and more badly put together than the ones in Clare's class.

Jinny felt sick with herself for seeing them like that. When she had lived in Stopton she would have loved to have owned any of them. They would have been beautiful to her then.

She brought Shantih to a walk behind one of the Highlands, hoping that the broad, black bottom would give her a feeling of security.

There were two judges – a weather-beaten man in a bowler, tweed jacket, breeches and gaiters who might have been made out of chewed leather, and a tall, sheepskinned lady.

When they were told to trot, Shantih tucked down her head and bucked. Jinny fought to stay on and managed it by the skin of her teeth. She gathered Shantih together and they tore round the ring at an extended trot. When they were asked to canter, Shantih galloped.

Jinny was brought in third. Two bay horses stood in front of her. A steward explained that they were to trot their horses down the ring, canter back, then dismount and remount.

The first bay gave a sober, gentlemanly performance. The second bay refused to canter.

It was Jinny's turn next. Looking straight ahead,

she rode Shantih out of the line and turned her to trot down the ring. Shantih cantered, fighting for her head. At the foot of the ring she reared, swung round and galloped back to the other horses. Jinny flung herself to the ground before she reached them, which was meant to be dismounting, and then remembered about her new jodhpurs. Hopping madly, she tried to get her foot into the stirrup. People round the ring began to laugh as Shantih plunged back to the other horses with Jinny, still hopping, at her side.

'Next,' said the steward.

'Wooden leg?' asked the man on the bay.

'It's my new jodhpurs,' Jinny announced loudly, glaring up at him. 'I can't bend my knee.'

Her voice carried round the ring and the laughter changed to applause. Scarlet-faced, Jinny had to wait until the steward gave her a leg up. She could imagine what Clare and her friends would be saying.

But that's it over, Jinny thought, *and I haven't come off*. And she waited impatiently until the other horses had given their displays.

'Don't we go now?' she asked the man on the bay when all the horses had had their turns.

'Judge has to ride them,' he said.

The chewed-leather judge came up to the first bay. The rider dismounted and the judge mounted. To Jinny's utter horror she saw that he was carrying a long cutting whip.

162

He can't ride Shantih with a whip, she thought. *I can't let him on her with a whip.*

Jinny couldn't think what to do, she could only sit and wait helplessly until the judge was standing in front of her.

'Now for the firecracker,' he said.

'I'm sorry,' said Jinny, 'you can't ride her with a whip. She's afraid of whips.'

'I won't use it,' said the judge, 'unless she needs it. I always carry a stick.'

'No,' said Jinny. 'She's terrified of them. You can't ride her with a whip in your hand.'

'Don't you say "can't" to me, my girl. Off you get. I'll not hurt your pony.'

'Oh, please understand,' said Jinny.

'Either I ride your horse or you are eliminated,' said the judge.

'Oh, I'll be eliminated,' agreed Jinny. 'That doesn't matter.'

The judge beckoned a steward over and spoke to him.

'Will number fifty-seven please leave the ring. This competitor is eliminated for refusing to comply with the rules of the show,' announced the steward over the loudspeaker.

Blushing scarlet and praying for an instant atom bomb to fall, Jinny tried to make Shantih leave the other horses.

'Here, what do you think you're at?' demanded the man on the bay when Shantih barged into him. 'Get over with you,' and he brought his stick down on Shantih's quarters.

Shantih bucked once, a violent, high, terrified buck. Jinny sailed over her head. The ground hit her hard, springing up to meet her, and as she lay there, stunned, she heard Shantih thundering out of the ring. Strangers crowded round Jinny asking if she was sure she hadn't hurt herself.

'I do it all the time,' Jinny assured them grimly as she got to her feet.

The people round the ring not only clapped but cheered and cat-called as Jinny trudged across the vast expanse of grass to the ring exit.

'But, my dear, what an exhibition!' exclaimed Clare.

'It was you who said I should have a go,' said Jinny, taking Shantih from Mr Burnley, who had caught her.

'Whatever happened?' demanded Clare. 'Why were you eliminated?'

'Wouldn't let the judge ride her. He had a stick.'

'Oh honestly!' cried Clare and the blond, pink-cheeked young man standing with her yawh, yawh, yawhed at the top of his voice.

'You are the weirdest kid I have ever known,' stated Clare.

'Yawh, yawh, yawh,' agreed the pink young man.

The show seemed to go on forever. Jinny stood

holding Shantih waiting for it to be over. People came up to make sure that she hadn't hurt herself, some to tell her that Shantih was wicked and not fit for a girl to ride, and some to ask if her new jodhpurs were still too tight. Clare and her friends paid no attention to her. They talked in their loud, waffling voices, telling each other how wonderful and pretty and sweet everything was. Jinny had thought of leading Shantih home, but she was afraid of the traffic on the Inverburgh road.

She watched as Clare, on Huston, won both jumping classes. She listened to Clare's friends telling her how jolly well she had ridden to win, although it was obvious that none of the horses had stood a chance against Huston.

It's not fair bringing such good horses to a small show like this, Jinny thought, *bringing them up from England*. But she only thought it because they were ignoring her. Jinny wanted to be part of the noise and bright excitement, to be the same as Clare's friends in their smart clothes, to make the same loud, empty noises, and to know the right things to say.

She wanted them to talk to her, to notice her, to tell her how sensible she had been in refusing to let the judge ride her horse. But not one of them paid any attention to Jinny or to Shantih as she pulled and fretted and whinnied.

'That's it for another year, what?' said Mr Burnley, when at last the mounted games had dragged to a close.

'Another year of triumph for you. Don't know what the locals would do if they didn't have you to give them a bit of competition?'

'Oh, I do absolutely adore Inverburgh Show,' sighed Clare. 'Now to get these fellows boxed. Let us hope your idiot doesn't take it into her head to play up,' and Clare looked with distaste at Shantih.

To Jinny's relief, Shantih followed Huston into the box as she had done in the morning – which seemed to Jinny to be a lifetime away.

In the high cabin Clare and her father talked to each other over Jinny's head. Twice she tried to join in but they paid no attention to her.

They think I'm a fool, Jinny decided. *And so I am. There's nothing about me that would make Clare want me for a friend, nothing about me that would interest Clare.*

But there was one thing. One thing that would interest them. Jinny dug her nails into the leather seat. She thought, *I mustn't tell them. I mustn't*, then she said in a voice that didn't sound like her own: 'Oh, by the way, I forgot to tell you, we've got two ospreys nesting on the moors.'

'You mean eagles,' said Clare.

'No, I don't. I mean ospreys. The RSPB men have seen them. They're ospreys OK.'

Both Clare and Mr Burnley were listening to her now. Jinny felt the day's disappointment and disgrace slip away as she began to tell the Burnleys all about the ospreys.

'Well, I'll eat my hat,' exclaimed Mr Burnley. 'What a turn up for the book. Wait till old Spencer hears this. And right under his very nose!'

Eleven

Jinny didn't tell her family much about the show. She knew they would eventually hear all about her exhibition from Mr MacKenzie, and she certainly didn't mention the fact that she had told the Burnleys about the ospreys. In fact, she tried not to think too much about that herself.

But the Burnleys wouldn't harm them. I know they wouldn't,' Jinny thought as she lay in bed. *They understand animals, they wouldn't harm them.*

Jinny turned over and tried to sleep but she couldn't. She lay thinking about the ospreys. She had promised not to tell anyone about them and she had broken her promise.

'But the Burnleys are different,' Jinny argued to herself. 'Quite, quite different. I'm allowed to tell them.'

Next morning, Jinny set off in good time for her

watch over the nest. Clare had said she would see to Shantih in the morning and Jinny was to ride to Craigvaar when she was off duty at four.

It makes it all so much easier, Jinny thought as she rode Bramble up the moors. *Now Clare knows what I'm doing I don't have to make excuses all the time. That was telling lies really.*

It was a bright spring day, with a blue sky and a breeze blowing through Jinny's hair and Bramble's mane, but as she rode, Jinny felt heavy and dead. She wanted to quarrel with someone, to get her temper out, but she didn't know what she was cross about, only felt it stored up inside her, sullen and black.

'I'll be glad when I'm back at school,' she thought. 'Glad when I've got Shantih back in her own paddock. Glad when Peter and Brian have gone away.'

She looked spitefully round at the moors and the mountains and, for the first time since they had come to Finmory, Jinny thought longingly of Stopton – of a Saturday matinée at the pictures with crisps and popcorn; of walking through the busy streets; of pushing her way on to a crowded bus and of being with people, lots of people who wouldn't care who she had told about the ospreys.

Instead of all this nothingness, thought Jinny. She kicked Bramble forward and he grunted and glowered.

'Get on with you when I tell you.' Jinny snarled at him. 'Get on with you, you old trekking pony.'

It's all the ospreys' fault, Jinny decided. *If they hadn't come and nested here I'd never have told Clare about them. It's all their fault.*

Mr Manders knew as soon as he saw Jinny riding towards the hide that she was in a bad mood. 'The sooner she brings Shantih back home and stops spending all her time with Clare Burnley the better I'll like it,' he said to himself. But he knew his daughter too well to say anything to her. 'What does she see in Clare?' he wondered, watching Jinny kicking the stubborn black bulk of Bramble up the hillside, and he was amazed yet again at how everything changed depending upon whose eyes you were looking through.

'This is *the* most stubborn beast,' exclaimed Jinny. 'Why one should have to ride such a creature I cannot think!'

Mr Manders struggled to keep his face straight. 'I presume you are speaking for Clare and yourself?' he asked.

'What?' said Jinny. 'Oh, I am so bored. I'm so bored with everything.'

'Are you?' said Mr Manders. 'Wonder why.'

Jinny looked quickly at her father, but there was no way he could possibly have found out that she had given away the ospreys' secret.

'Don't know,' said Jinny. 'I'm just fed up.'

'No more sign of your birdwatcher,' said Mr Manders. 'He must have given up. Well, don't be falling asleep,' and he climbed onto Bramble and rode away.

'Fed up, fed up, fed up,' muttered Jinny, as she fixed the glasses on the ospreys. The male was on his favourite perch, the female deep in the nest with only her head and tail visible.

Buck up and hatch them, Jinny thought. *Hurry up and get away from here. Stupid birds.*

Through the glasses Jinny saw the cock turn to stare directly at her, almost as if he could read her thoughts, then she heard the sound of hooves. For a moment Jinny thought her father must have forgotten something, but the trampling hooves sounded more like several horses and not just Bramble.

'Coo-ee, Jinny,' called Clare's voice, and the male osprey flapped into the air.

For a second, Jinny couldn't move. She couldn't imagine what Clare was doing on the moors so close to the ospreys. What if her father had seen her? Jinny felt a cold guilty sweat prickling her skin. She stumbled out of the hide. Clare, riding Huston and leading Jasper, was only a few yards away.

'Gosh, I thought I'd never find you,' cried Clare. 'I'll say this for you, you've made a jolly good job of the hide.'

'What do you want?' demanded Jinny. 'You're disturbing the ospreys.'

'Sorry. Am I being terribly naughty?'

Jinny stared uneasily at Clare. 'Dad was here a few

minutes ago. If he'd seen you he would have been mad with me. I told you yesterday it was a secret.'

'Gosh, yes,' said Clare. 'Only it's a sort of emergency. I've come for you. Ma was speaking to Lady Gilbert on the phone this morning and we've been invited to visit her for lunch.'

'We? I don't know Lady Gilbert.'

'Of course you do. You must have heard of her Arabs. They're famous. And when she lives so close. Normally she won't let anyone near them, she's utterly possessive about them. So when she asked us over for lunch I knew you would be mad if you missed such a chance, and I grabbed the phone from Ma and told Lady G. about Shantih, and how well you are doing with her, and she is just crazy to meet you.'

'But I can't come,' said Jinny. She had read about Lady Gilbert's Arabs winning prizes at the Arab Horse Show but she had never thought she would have a chance of visiting her stables. 'I'm on duty here. I can't leave the nest.'

'Oh, for goodness' sake grow up!' exclaimed Clare. 'Here I am offering you the chance of a lifetime and all you say is "I can't come". Why ever not? You want to see the Arabs, don't you?'

'Of course,' said Jinny crossly. 'Of course I do. But I can't.'

'Look, I've dragged these horses all over the moors so you can ride back with me.'

'I tell you I can't come.'

'You don't need to worry about your old chickens. There's never a soul on these moors. They're as safe as the Bank of England. I mean you can't, you just cannot, turn down a chance like this. To see Lady Gilbert's Arabs, to see her stallion.'

'Her stallion?' echoed Jinny. 'Has she got a stallion?'

'She has,' said Clare and waited.

'I would have to be back before half-past three. Ken comes up at four.'

'Lord, it's only eleven. Look, I give you my word you'll be back here before four. That's if you come now and stop all this boring fuss. Here, you have Huston,' and Clare jumped down and handed the grey's reins to Jinny.

'I shouldn't, honestly I shouldn't,' said Jinny. She hesitated, looking at the ospreys' nest. 'If anything happened to them . . .'

'Oh, it won't,' said Clare. 'I mean to say, no one would expect you to stay here when you've the chance of seeing an Arab stud.'

'We *must* be back before four,' said Jinny, pulling herself up onto Huston. 'My family would murder me if they ever found out I'd left them alone.'

For a second Jinny hesitated, torn between going with Clare, which she knew was wrong, and staying on guard, which she knew was right. The Burnleys' car might have a puncture or anything might happen to delay them, to stop Jinny being in the hide when Ken arrived at four. But what really mattered were the ospreys' eggs. If anything happened to them while she was with Clare, it would be her fault.

Jinny leaned her weight on the pommel of Huston's saddle, ready to swing herself to the ground. 'I can't come. I must stay and watch the nest.' The words were in her mind. She opened her mouth to say them.

'I expect there will be one or two foals by now,' said Clare.

'Foals! Arab foals!' and Jinny was trotting Huston at Jasper's side. 'I've never seen an Arab foal.'

Lady Gilbert's home was almost a castle – towers and turrets and slit windows set in the thickness of the walls.

Clare tugged at the heavy metal bell-pull and the noise jangled and echoed through the corridors. Lady Gilbert was stiff and elderly, and Jinny thought she didn't seem very pleased to see them. They sat in straight-backed chairs in a room that smelt of spaniels. Clare and Lady Gilbert made polite noises at each other while Jinny thought about the ospreys, wondered when they were going to see the Arabs, and tried to look as if she were interested in the conversation.

Clare and Lady Gilbert had a sherry, Lady Gilbert presumed that the child would not want one. Then they went down to a vast dining hall with a huge, polished oak table in it. At one end of the table three places were set for lunch. Lady Gilbert sat at the head of the table, Jinny and Clare on either side of her. A very old man creaked in, carrying the different courses. If Jinny had been at home she could have finished each plateful in two or three mouthfuls, but Lady Gilbert ate very slowly, putting down the heavy cutlery every time she stopped eating to talk to Clare.

A grandfather clock struck two as they got up from the table.

'Watson will serve coffee in my room,' said Lady Gilbert, and began to climb the stairs back to the room they had been in earlier.

'That's two o'clock,' Jinny muttered to Clare. 'I told you I *must* be back at the hide by half-past three at the absolute latest. I *must*, Clare. And we haven't seen the Arabs yet.'

'What does the child say?' asked Lady Gilbert, stopping on the stairs and turning round to regard Jinny.

'She's hoping to see your horses,' said Clare.

'Is she? Is she now?' said Lady Gilbert.

'I have an Arab,' said Jinny. 'I would love to see yours.'

'Indeed,' said Lady Gilbert and turned back to her slow ascent.

Watson brought the coffee in a silver coffee pot and Lady Gilbert poured it out into tiny cups. It was strong and bitter. Jinny sat on the edge of her chair trying to catch Clare's eye. It had taken them at least an hour to reach here and it would take them another hour to drive back to Craigvaar and then Jinny still had to get to the hide.

'Does your dear mother have difficulty in finding the right type of girl?' Lady Gilbert asked Clare. 'I interview them all personally. I have never had a housemaid in service here whom I have not interviewed myself.'

Come on, come on, come on, thought Jinny. *When are we going to see the Arabs? I must get back. I must.*

She searched the room for clocks, found one, and saw to her horror that it was half-past two.

'It's half-past two!' she exclaimed, her voice coming out louder than she had meant it to be.

Lady Gilbert paused, looked curiously at Jinny, and went on talking to Clare.

'We've got to go,' said Jinny standing up. 'I'm sorry to interrupt, but I must be back home for four. Clare knows I can't stay any longer than this. I told her I had to be back.'

'What is upsetting the child?' Lady Gilbert said to Clare. 'Is she unwell?'

'Oh, I say, I do apologise,' said Clare, 'but I'm afraid that we will have to go. She has an appointment with the dentist for four o'clock.'

'Sweets,' said Lady Gilbert. 'The ruin of children's teeth. Never allowed mine to touch them.'

What a bloomin' lie, thought Jinny, but she didn't care about anything except being back at the hide before Ken arrived. She wanted to pull Clare downstairs and into the car and make her drive at a hundred miles per hour. Anything, as long as Jinny was back at the hide for four.

'Could we go out through your stable yard?' Clare asked as they said goodbye.

'What an extraordinary request,' murmured Lady Gilbert. 'Do tell your dear mother how sorry I was that she was unable to accompany you.'

'Can we see your Arabs?' asked Jinny. Really, she didn't care any more, but it seemed such a waste when she had come especially to see them.

Lady Gilbert looked at her distantly. 'You are a very impertinent little girl,' she said. 'I never allow strangers near my horses. Never.'

'But you said you'd asked. That you'd asked her on the phone if I could see them and that she'd said I could.' Jinny's hands were clenched into fists, she was sitting on them hard as Clare drove back to Craigvaar. 'You said we'd see her stallion. And foals. You told me she wanted to hear about Shantih!'

'Well, I did warn you that she was rather eccentric,' said Clare.

'I wouldn't call her eccentric. She seemed to me to know exactly what she was doing. I would never have come if you hadn't promised we'd see the Arabs. I wanted to see the stallion.' But the only thing Jinny wanted now was to get back to the hide before Ken arrived. 'Can't you go any faster?'

'No, I cannot,' said Clare. 'One thing's certain, if we're copped for speeding you certainly won't be back in time.'

Jinny stared through the windscreen, willing the car to greater speed. She kept glancing at Clare's watch, seeing its hands creeping steadily to three and then down towards a quarter past.

'I should never have come. I knew I shouldn't have left the nest.'

'Oh, dry up,' said Clare. 'I never met anyone who made a fuss about every single thing the way you do. If you'd been at my boarding school you'd jolly soon have learned to do things that the mistresses didn't know about. What does it matter what your precious Ken says? He won't jolly well eat you, will he?'

At last the car reached Craigvaar. Jinny wrenched the door open. She saw to her surprise that Spencer was standing at the front door, but she hadn't time to think about it, hadn't even time to go and see Shantih. The minute Jinny was out of the car she was running full speed over the moors in the direction of Loch Varrich. She had half an hour in which to reach the hide.

Stumbling and breathless, Jinny raced across the moors.

'If Ken is there I'll tell him that I was feeling sick, that I just went for a walk to get out of the hide for a bit.' The rough going slowed Jinny to a walk. She fought her way on up the hillside, panting for breath, pulling herself up, using her hands as well as her feet.

She was mad with herself. Why had she told the Burnleys about the ospreys? Why had she gone with Clare? Jinny didn't know.

Getting her second wind, she broke into a run again. *Oh, please don't let him be there*, she thought. *Please let me get there first.*

Jinny staggered over the hilltop above the loch. She paused to look quickly round for any sign of Ken approaching on one of the ponies but there was nothing. Jinny gasped with relief. She freewheeled down to the hide, and ducked in at the doorway. It was empty. Everything was exactly as she had left it.

Jinny collapsed on to the box, and sat for a few moments until she got her breath back. She was there before Ken. No one would ever know she had been away.

She looked out through the slit in the hide. Both ospreys were flying above their nest. Jinny had never seen them behaving like this before. She snatched up the glasses, focused them, and saw the ospreys wheeling round the nest in obvious distress. Jinny froze with horror. She could see nothing that could be disturbing them. Then she saw that part of the nest seemed to have been broken off. She could see the sticks lying scattered at the foot of the tree.

Jinny dropped the glasses. She ran down the hill to the pine trees. The ospreys' cries of distress and alarm were loud in the still air. As Jinny reached the nest one of the birds swooped towards her. Jinny caught a glimpse of its gaping beak, the useless, wordless strip of its tongue, before it flung itself upwards again, screaming with fury.

A great lump had been broken out of the side of the nest. It lay scattered at Jinny's feet. Close beside the sticks was a smashed egg. The yolk had already begun to knot itself into an osprey embryo.

The parent birds screamed and cried around Jinny as she stood staring down at it. While she had been away someone had destroyed the nest. No matter who had done it, it had been Jinny's fault that it had happened. If she hadn't left the nest unguarded the egg would have gone on growing until it became a great hawk, able to ride the air, to live wild and free and self-contained. But now, because she had gone with Clare, this could never happen. Jinny felt cold and sick.

She would have to go home and tell them what she had done. She turned away, and, walking very slowly, made her way back to Finmory.

Twelve

Mrs Manders was standing by the sink when Jinny walked into the kitchen. Mike was sitting at the table, cutting out pictures of space rockets from a Sunday newspaper supplement.

'You were quick,' said Mike. 'Ken hasn't been gone long.'

'What's wrong?' asked Mrs Manders, seeing Jinny's face. 'Has something happened to Shantih?'

Jinny shut the door and leant against it. She looked at her mother but couldn't find the words to tell her what had happened.

'I didn't mean to,' Jinny said. 'Honestly I didn't mean to.'

Her father came into the kitchen to see who had arrived.

'Something wrong?' he asked.

Jinny's face was drained of colour, her eyes huge in her pinched face.

'I didn't mean to do it,' she repeated.

'Do what?' asked her mother, going over to Jinny. 'Come and sit down and tell us about it. See if we can help.'

'You can't,' said Jinny, wishing she could cry, for that would make it easier, but what she had done was too bad to be smoothed over with tears. 'I didn't stay at the hide. I went with Clare to Lady Gilbert's. And the eggs have gone. The nest's broken and one of the eggs is smashed. And I think the others have gone too.'

'Oh, Jinny,' said her mother. 'Why did you do that? If you'd told us you wanted to go somewhere with Clare we could have arranged for someone else to be at the hide.'

'I didn't know,' said Jinny. 'I met her on the moors.'

'Better wake Brian and Peter,' said Mr Manders. 'Maybe we can find the fool that took them. Just a chance that he might still be hiding on the hills somewhere.'

'They'll be raving,' said Mike. 'After all the nights they've sat up and you had to go and do this.'

In minutes, Brian and Peter came running downstairs. They pulled on wellingtons and set off over the moors. Mr Manders and Mike went with them.

'I didn't mean to,' Jinny said to her mother after they had gone.

'But you did it,' said her mother. 'And it can't be changed now.'

'I only wanted to see Lady Gilbert's Arabs and we never saw them anyway.'

'You know you were trusted to look after the nest and you left it unguarded. You knew what you were doing was wrong. There's no way round that. You chose to do what you knew was wrong.'

When Jinny heard them coming back from the nest she wondered if she should go and hide in her bedroom, but she knew that would be no use. She sat still and waited.

They all came into the kitchen. For a moment there was silence, then Brian and Peter began to tell Jinny what they thought about her.

'Why didn't you tell us from the beginning that you weren't interested? Of all the sneaky, rotten things to do, to pretend you were going to keep watch and then to go off and leave them. When you'd only to lift the walkie-talkie and tell us that you were going. One of us would have been up in half an hour. You could have gone for the whole day then. If you'd only waited half an hour. All bloomin' wasted now. If the ospreys have any sense they won't come back here. All bloomin' wasted because of your selfishness.'

'You might as well have taken a gun and shot them,' said Peter. 'You killed them.'

'I know,' said Jinny despairingly. 'Oh, I do know. But

I didn't mean to. If I'd shot them I'd have meant to shoot them.'

'When a thing is destroyed it doesn't make much difference why it was destroyed – it's good and dead. There ain't going to be no young ospreys now, and that, sister, is that. The ospreys don't know whether you *meant* to abandon their eggs or not. Whether you *meant* to go off enjoying yourself when you should have been guarding their nest. They only know what's happened.'

Jinny stared down at her hands, hating herself.

'Who could have taken them?' asked Mrs Manders. 'Who would want to destroy like that?'

'Who knew about them?' asked Mike.

'It wasn't the man from the gift shop,' said Mr Manders. 'Brian knows him.'

'Lives quite close to my area,' said Brian. 'Drops in from time to time to tell me of any rare birds he's seen. Compare notes. Not a chance on this earth that he'd touch the eggs.'

'Who then?' insisted Mike. 'We didn't tell anyone.'

'You told the Burnleys,' said the voice in Jinny's head.

'But they wouldn't have touched the eggs. The Burnleys wouldn't do a thing like that,' Jinny replied indignantly.

'But you told them,' insisted the voice. 'Perhaps they told someone else and they stole them.'

Jinny looked round miserably at her family. *At least they don't know about that*, she thought guiltily.

'Maybe one of the farmer's pals,' suggested Peter. 'Though from what you said he seems the type who would keep his mouth shut.'

'Well, there's no more we can do about it,' said Brian bitterly. 'Jot it down to experience and learn the lesson that you keep watch yourself. Or share it with experienced people you know you can trust.'

'It's early enough in the season. They might find another nest site. Let's hope they do,' said Peter.

'And that they've the sense to clear out of this district before the lunatic returns and finishes off the birds as well.'

When Petra got back she, too, was loud in expressing her opinion about her sister's behaviour.

'I just don't know how you could do such a thing,' she said over and over again, as if she was pleased with herself for not knowing.

'Well neither do I,' said Jinny, probed at last into answering back. 'I expect we all do things we don't mean to do. I didn't mean to harm the ospreys. It wasn't me that took the eggs.' And she went to bed to dream of the judge from the Inverburgh Show chasing Shantih up a pine tree and then catching her and breaking her like an egg.

Jinny got up early the next morning. She had breakfast before anyone else was up and walked to

Craigvaar. Shantih came rushing to the box door; whinnying to her. Jinny clapped her neck, rubbed her hands lovingly over her face and breathed in the warm sweet smell of her breath.

'Oh, you'd understand how it happened,' Jinny said to her. 'You do things that you don't mean to do. You'd understand.'

Jinny mucked out the three horses, gave them water and an armful of hay, then sat in Shantih's box talking to her.

Spencer came into the yard first. He looked at Jinny with unconcealed surprise.

'Good lord,' he said. 'Clare didn't tell me you were in residence.'

Jinny regarded him uncertainly. She had managed to rearrange the past so that it was Spencer who had galloped off leaving her lying in the road. She was almost sure now that Clare had wanted to stay and see that she hadn't hurt herself.

'How kind,' Clare said when she saw that Jinny had mucked out. 'But of course, now that Spencer's back, we can really manage this sort of thing ourselves. And I do wish you wouldn't give them so much hay. I know your nag needs filling out, but when we're going to exercise them straight after breakfast we don't want them stuffed up with hay.'

Clare and Spencer tacked up their horses.

'Could I bring Shantih?' Jinny asked Clare.

'Shantih?' said Clare. 'Oh, I don't think so. I mean to say, it isn't that we wouldn't love to have you with us, but now Spencer's back we'll be having a gallop over the moors and you don't want to damage her wind, do you?'

Jinny stood and watched them ride out of the yard together, their horses stepping out, their tack gleaming, with bits and stirrups glinting in the sun. She still saw them as if they were bright with gold dust, a brightness about them that ordinary people didn't have. Anything they did must surely be right because they were the Burnleys.

Jinny took Shantih down to the paddock and concentrated on her riding, blanking off the thought of the smashed egg and the ospreys' cries of distress. Although Shantih had several bucking outbursts Jinny didn't come off. In all the disgrace that was surrounding Jinny the thought that Shantih was improving was like a tiny chink of light in a long dark tunnel.

Later in the morning, while Clare was grooming Jasper, Jinny told her about how the ospreys' nest had been robbed while they had been at Lady Gilbert's.

'No!' exclaimed Clare, 'I cannot believe it. Is no-where safe from them?'

'Them?' demanded Jinny, thinking Clare knew of some gang of international egg collectors.

'Why, the yobs and vandals, of course. Who else would do a thing like that? But it does mean that you won't have to do any more of that dreary guard duty. Actually, Spencer and I are going out this afternoon, so I was going to say that would leave you free to watch your nest, but I suppose that will be a thing of the past now.'

'They won't lay again in that nest this year,' said Jinny.

'Oh, well, if you want to hang around here do, but we shan't be here so it does seem a bit pointless.'

Jinny stayed to groom Shantih and then she went home. She took her drawing pad and went to sit in the ponies' field but her pencil was clumsy in her fingers. She was only wasting paper so she stopped and sat staring at the sea until it was supper time.

Peter and Brian had left.

'There was no sign of the ospreys this morning so they reckoned there was no point in waiting on here. Both had plenty of work to do,' said Mr Manders.

'They left this envelope for you,' said Petra. 'Said I was to give it to you when they'd gone.'

Jinny took the envelope unwillingly. She couldn't think what they could have left for her. She opened it, feeling for a letter, but the envelope was empty except for something in one corner. Jinny tipped it up and a fragment of eggshell fell into her palm. She stared down at it, tears blinding her, then she turned and dashed upstairs to her room.

Lying stretched out on her bed she buried her head

in the pillow and cried. She cried for the ospreys that would have hatched out of the eggs to fly high and clear over the moors and the sea, that might have come back to Finmory to build their own nests and breed their own young. But her own selfishness had spoiled it all. She might have watched the fledglings grow and fly. But now there was nothing.

Yet Jinny wasn't only crying for the ospreys, she was crying because Clare and Spencer had ridden out of the yard on their bright horses and she hadn't been with them. They hadn't wanted her.

When Mike came up to tell her supper was ready Jinny had scrubbed her eyes dry.

'That was a rotten thing to do,' said Mike. 'You shouldn't have left the hide but they didn't need to do that.'

'I expect that's how they felt about me,' said Jinny. She blew her nose hard and went down for her supper.

'But your horse just isn't fit to keep up with ours. Asking for broken wind galloping an unfit horse,' said Clare the next morning when Jinny wanted to ride with the Burnleys.

'She galloped from here to Loch Varrich,' said Jinny.

'Well, one wouldn't want that to happen again, would one?'

Jinny supposed one wouldn't. She knew Clare didn't want her and yet she couldn't stop herself from begging Clare to pay attention to her.

It's so useless, Jinny thought. *When I don't like a person, the more they try to make me like them the more I can't stand them, so there's no point in trying to make Clare like me.* But somehow she couldn't stop herself pleading with Clare.

'Could I come part of the way with you, and if it's too much for Shantih I'll come back?'

'Oh honestly!' exclaimed Clare. 'I've told you. She isn't fit. Take her down to the paddock and do stop being such a bore. I let you use my paddock. I feed your horse. What more do you expect?'

Jinny waited until Spencer and Clare had clattered out of the yard, then she put on Shantih's tack and rode her home. Shantih was pleased to be going back to Finmory, back to her own field, to Punch and Bramble. She walked out with a long striding step, and when Jinny asked her to trot she went forward without any nonsense, going kindly into a steady jog.

'So you've had enough of your fancy friends?' Mr MacKenzie called as Jinny rode Shantih past his farm.

'They've had enough of me,' answered Jinny. 'Clare's got Spencer back now.'

'That'll be the way of it,' said Mr MacKenzie. 'Did I not tell you it was the toffs you were dealing with when you were taking to do with the Burnleys?'

Jinny rode slowly back to Finmory and turned Shantih out into the field. The Highlands came trotting over, whinnying a welcome, and in no time they had their heads down grazing. Jinny watched them for a moment or two then went indoors.

'I've brought Shantih home,' she said to her mother.

'That's good,' said Mrs Manders. 'Not be long before you're back at school. You'll need to start and get your things ready. Did you thank Clare for all her help?'

'Huh,' exclaimed Jinny. 'Clare won't even notice I've gone. She's got Spencer now.'

'Well, she is much older than you and she has been very kind.'

But Jinny hadn't wanted anyone to be kind to her. She had wanted to be part of the Burnleys' life, to be Clare's friend, to ride as well as Clare, to know all the things Clare knew about horses and, most of all, she had wanted Clare to admire Shantih – to see her as Jinny saw her, a golden, magic horse. That was what Jinny wanted and that was why she had told them about the ospreys.

But now it was all over, all hopeless. Never again would Jinny ride with Clare or stand in her stable yard listening to her stories of all the cups she had won and all the horses she had ridden.

Jinny stared blankly through the kitchen window. The whole world seemed grey and empty. There was nothing in it that was worth doing when she couldn't ride with Clare.

Thirteen

'You'll be for Craigvaar tomorrow?' Mr MacKenzie asked Jinny.

'Why?'

'Why? To wave goodbye to your friends. I was hearing they'll be off back to England.'

'Will they?' said Jinny as if she didn't care.

'Aye, they will, and you'll be off back to the school. And a good job too, I'm thinking. Your head's been filled with the nonsense these holidays.'

'Has it?' said Jinny.

'Indeed it has. Taking that wild horse of yours to the show – I never heard such nonsense in my life. And a fair carry-on you've had over the sea eagles. Though I'm thinking maybe that wee bit of business was not altogether your fault.'

'It was,' said Jinny.

As Jinny walked home with the milk she thought that she would have to go to Craigvaar tomorrow to return the martingale and drop noseband that Clare had lent her. She supposed she should have thanked Clare. Perhaps it had been rude just riding off like that. *Not that Clare would have noticed*, Jinny thought. *She wanted to get rid of me.*

Next morning Jinny rode round the back of Craigvaar and into the stable yard through the paddock. Shantih whinnied and, with a clatter of hooves, Jasper and Huston were looking out over their half doors. Jinny was pleased to see that they weren't being exercised. When they were in their boxes it meant that Clare would be around somewhere. Jinny jumped down from Shantih and waited a moment or two, hoping that Clare would have heard her and appear, but there was no sign of her.

'Clare,' Jinny called, 'Clare?'

But no one answered. Jinny hesitated, uncertain what to do next. She led Shantih into the loose box and took off the martingale and drop noseband.

'If the gift shop manages to sell my drawings and Nell takes some more, I'll buy you a martingale,' Jinny said to Shantih, who was more interested in getting to the door to rub noses with Huston.

Jinny went back out into the yard and called again but still no one answered. She wondered if she could leave the martingale and noseband on the tack room table – Clare would know where they had come from. But Jinny knew this would be taking the easy way out. She had to give the tack to Clare.

Jinny stared round the yard, remembering the morning when they had all set off for the Inverburgh Show; the day Clare had said she had a good seat; the day she had jumped Huston; the days of exercising the horses with Clare when they had ridden together through the spring sunshine. Jinny heard Clare's voice in her ears telling her all about the ponies and horses she had ridden, all the shows she had been to, all the cups she had won, and the great leaps she had taken when she was giving the field a lead out hunting. For a last time Jinny looked round the yard, imagining that it all belonged to her – the loose boxes, the horsebox, the tack room with its gleaming saddles and bridles and rows of rosettes pinned to the walls and, best of all, the three horses, Huston to jump, Jasper to show and Shantih because she was herself and Jinny loved her.

Jinny gave herself a shake. She walked quickly through the shrubbery and over the lawns to the house. There was no one to be seen at the windows or at the back door. Jinny hesitated awkwardly, wondering if anyone was watching her, holding out the martingale so that anyone seeing her would know why she was there.

She decided to go round to the front door. It was

standing half open. Jinny knocked and stood back, hoping that Spencer wouldn't be the one to answer it. Mrs Burnley would be the easiest. She would tell Jinny how wonderfully pretty her hair was and Jinny could thank her and hand back the tack.

It was Heather, the Burnleys' housekeeper, who came to the door. She was a warm, kindly woman who had always made Jinny feel welcome.

'You'll be wanting to see Clare?' Heather said.

'Yes,' said Jinny. 'I've come to give these back to her.'

'Och, come in then,' said Heather. 'We've all been wondering where you went off to in such a hurry. Clare was in the drawing room a minute ago. In you go and wait and I'll be telling her you're here.'

Jinny rubbed her wellingtons on the mat and followed Heather inside.

'Wait you there for a moment and I'll find Clare for you,' said Heather, opening the drawing room door.

Jinny stepped carefully over the pale primrose carpet on to the black hearth rug. The morning sun streamed through the double-glazed windows, filling the room with light. All the furniture was tastefully modern. You could tell that the people who lived here read the right advertisements. On top of a long, low sideboard were photographs of Clare and Spencer on their ponies. Jinny went over to have a look at them.

Lying on the sideboard was an open box. Inside it, carefully padded with cotton wool, were two cream-

coloured eggs marked with brownish purple blotches
– ospreys' eggs.

Jinny stared at them in disbelief. They couldn't be, couldn't possibly be . . . she felt cold and sick and wanted to run away from them. Never to have seen them. Not to know about them. Never, ever to know about them for it could not be true.

'No! Oh no!' breathed Jinny. She stretched her hand out and touched the ospreys' eggs with her finger, felt their porous texture. 'No,' she said again. 'No,' as if by denying them she could make them vanish. But the eggs were real.

Jinny stood drowning in the same horror as she had felt when she had seen the smashed egg lying at the foot of the tree. The useless, pointless killing engulfed her, this sad and stupid waste. Left in the nest the eggs would have hatched into ospreys, now they were no more than lifeless objects, senseless possessions.

'Oh no,' said Jinny, unable to believe it.

The door opened and Clare came in.

'Well, hello,' she said. 'We couldn't think what had happened to you, vanishing like that . . .' Then she realised that Jinny had seen the eggs. 'Oh Lord,' said Clare. 'This jolly well would have to happen.'

'It was Spencer,' cried Jinny. 'It was Spencer who stole the eggs. You told him about the nest and you made it all up about Lady Gilbert being interested in

Shantih and wanting me to see her Arabs. You made it all up so that I'd leave the ospreys unguarded and Spencer could take the eggs.'

'He is frightfully keen on birds' eggs. Always has been,' said Clare. 'And I mean to say, the chance of ospreys' eggs laid in Scotland – it was just asking too much of anyone not to jump at the chance.'

'You came up specially to take me away from the hide. All the time we were at Lady Gilbert's you knew what Spencer was doing. And you must have phoned him. *You* must have phoned him and told him to come back here because of the eggs.'

'Now look here,' said Clare. 'Do be sensible about this . . .'

'How could you?' cried Jinny. 'How could you do such a rotten thing! They would have been ospreys. They would have been *ospreys*.'

And suddenly words were not enough to express Jinny's disgust. She grabbed the eggs out of the box, one in each hand, and before Clare could stop her Jinny had thrown them down and stamped on them, smashing them to fragments. Then she ducked under Clare's outstretched arm, dodged through the door, ran out of the house and was tearing down the garden to Shantih almost before she knew that she intended to smash the eggs.

Spencer was standing at Jasper's box.

'You rotten thief,' Jinny yelled at him and his eyes

flickered over her, dry and emotionless as a lizard's. 'It was my fault but you killed them.'

Jinny tugged up Shantih's girths and raced out of the yard.

'Stop her,' bawled Clare, crashing through the rhododendrons. 'She's jolly well smashed the eggs.'

But Jinny was through the paddock gate. She flung herself on to Shantih's back and they were galloping over the moor as fast as they had on Shantih's first mad gallop away from Clare.

When they were well clear of Craigvaar Jinny steadied Shantih to a walk. All the things she hadn't allowed herself to see before came flooding into her mind. Clare bringing expensive horses up from England to win cups at a small show; Clare riding off with Spencer, leaving Jinny lying on the road; Clare's voice saying that she wouldn't care to be seen on Shantih; Clare's temper; the speed with which she had cast Jinny off when Spencer came home and the way she had tricked Jinny over the ospreys. Jinny didn't know why she had wanted to be so blind.

For a last time she glimpsed her golden image of Clare – and then it had gone. Clare was only a lumpish girl with heavy hands who wanted her own way all the time and didn't care how she got it. The exclusive, select life of the Burnleys that had haunted Jinny since her first glimpse of it had lost its magic. They were loud and selfish and Jinny knew what she would think if any of her own family behaved the way the Burnleys did. The golden bubble had burst.

Jinny put Shantih into her box, gave her a scoopful of nuts and went in to tell her family what had happened, to tell them the whole truth.

Everyone except Ken was in the kitchen.

'I know who took the eggs,' Jinny said. 'Spencer Burnley. I told Clare about the ospreys and she told him and he took them.'

'Oh, Jinny,' said her father. 'You told Clare? But why? Why?'

'I wanted them to like me,' said Jinny, and she told them all that had happened. It was like taking off layers and layers of heavy clothing that had been stifling her and being able to move again, being able to breathe.

'Well, it's all over now,' said her mother when Jinny had reached the end of her confession. 'Let's hope you've learned something from it. You do get yourself tangled up in things.'

'Oh, don't I?' agreed Jinny wearily.

She led Shantih down to the field and leaned over the gate watching her. She could see her again as her own horse and it was herself, Jinny Manders, and no one else, who had to find a way to ride her and school her and help her to understand how to live with humans.

'Nice to have you back,' said Ken, coming to stand by the gate. 'Mike told me.'

'I didn't mean to harm the ospreys.'

'They'll come back,' said Ken.

'Will they?' asked Jinny, seeking reassurance.

'You know that yourself,' said Ken. 'Open your eyes. Summer into winter. Winter into spring. That's the way it is.'

And suddenly it didn't seem quite so bad. After all, Jinny thought, there was the summer holidays when she would do better than she had these holidays. Much better.

'Perhaps if the gift shop takes some more of my drawings I'll buy a proper lunge rein,' she said.

Ken laughed, throwing back his head, taken by ridiculous, total laughter, making Shantih look up, the tips of her ears pointed in surprise. She gazed steadily at them through her dark, lustrous eyes, then whisked her tail and went back to her grazing.

'Knowing you, you'll find a way,' said Ken.

'I will,' said Jinny. 'Oh yes, I will.'

EDITOR'S NOTE

Humans have been falling in love with horses for centuries – Jinny and Shantih, created in the 1970s are relative newcomers to the scene.

Here at Catnip we feel that this series was ahead of its time and is as fresh and relevant today as when it was first published. For this reason we have left Patricia Leitch's text in its original, startlingly beautiful, form.

Some of the cultural references reflect the time in which the books were written: Jinny references Enoch Powell, a politician active between 1950-1974 and a pair of jodhpurs can cost just five pounds. Yet the social issues and emotions tackled in each book are as timeless as the spiritual bond between girl and horse.

Jinny at Finmory

For Love of a Horse

> "One of the best series of pony books ever written. Fresh, relevant and timeless."
>
> Lauren St John

Patricia Leitch

FOR LOVE OF A HORSE

*The horse was a pure-bred Arab. She came,
bright and dancing, flaunting into the ring,
her tail held high over her quarters, her silken
mane flowing over the crest of her neck.*

When Jinny Manders moves to wilds of
Finmory in the Scottish Highlands she has
only one dream: a pony of her own. That's
until a near-wild chestnut Arab steals her heart.
But it seems the mare will never trust her,
even though Jinny would risk everything
to save the horse she loves.

RAVEN BOY
by Pippa Goodhart

Legend has it that if the ravens leave the Tower of London, monarch and kingdom will fall.

London 1666, the Great Plague rages and the city is a dangerous place. Young Nick Truelove blames his King, Charles II, and vows revenge.

Inspired by the cunning of a young raven, Nick bluffs his way into the centre of the King's power, the Tower of London itself.

But, as a remarkable friendship grows up between boy and raven, a new danger engulfs the city. Nick's view of the world and his King is about to be changed for ever.

"This fast-moving adventure is rich with historical detail" THE GUARDIAN

DRAGON RACER
by Margaret Bateson-Hill

Joanna Morris's life is about to change forever.
School, homework, even her family take
second place when she shoots to stardom as
the youngest racing dragon flyer in the country.

Flying Excelsior, the beautiful silver
spiked-back dragon, is more exciting that
anything she's ever known, and he's soon the
best friend she's ever had.

But beneath the glamour and beauty of
dragon racing lie terrible jealousies and
resentments and Joanna and Excelsior are
soon in grave danger.

*"An out-of-this-world-exciting story about
friendship and loyalty."* LOVEREADING4KIDS

You can find out more about other
exciting Catnip books by visiting:

www.catnippublishing.co.uk